Technical Report Writing

This stack of volumes, nearly five feet high and containing 13,200 pages, is a single report on antenna research for the Titan III space booster, conducted by Lockheed-Georgia's Antenna Laboratory.

Technical Report Writing

RUFUS P. TURNER

California State College at Los Angeles

Holt, Rinehart and Winston

New York   Chicago   San Francisco   Toronto   London

To

Walter M. Crittenden

Distinguished Teacher

Preface

The art of report writing must be mastered as quickly as possible by a great many people in science and industry. Students, practicing engineers and scientists, and some technicians must write effective reports as a regular part of their work, and the upgrading of these people hinges largely upon their good reporting.

A person best learns to write by trying his hand at it — practicing ardently and criticizing his work cold-bloodedly — and this approach is to be encouraged. However, he also needs guideposts. This book tries to supply them, in providing the rudiments of technical report writing and standard professional practices, along with many illustrative examples and writing exercises.

The book presupposes, as college curricula do, that technical report writing is an upper-division course and that the student comes to it fortified by at least one course in English composition. Therefore no space is wasted on language mechanics. When the reader is cautioned, as he is in Chapter 1, for example, that he should avoid circumlocutions, it is assumed that he already knows what a circumlocution is. The student or writer who needs to refresh his grammar, as many do, is referred to my *Grammar Review for Technical Writers* (Holt, Rinehart and Winston, 1964), a companion to the present book.

The text employs a combination of description and direction which I have found effective in teaching, and I hope that the unpatterned alternation between the two modes will not be construed as a shift in point of view. Question-and-answer tests are shunned in favor of actual writing exercises at the end of chapters. Many readers will use the text as a handbook, going only to a needed chapter, and it is to serve them that some repetition has been permitted.

I express here my gratitude to several companies and individuals for valued illustrative material: *Electronic Industries* Magazine, Douglas Aircraft Company, Inc. (Missile and Space Systems Division), Hughes Aircraft Company (Electronic Properties Information Center: EPIC), Weston Instruments & Electronics (Division of Daystrom, Inc.), Mr. Robert J. Bramlett, Mr. H. Thayne Johnson, Mr. Walter W. Keim, and Mr. J. L. Straight.

Altadena, California   RUFUS P. TURNER
January 1965

Contents

Chapter 9. Revising and Rewriting   91

Chapter 10. Preparing the Final Draft   104

List of Illustrations

1

Introduction

Technical writing as a profession is growing. Its existence can hardly go unnoticed, since its name regularly appears now in all sorts of places — want ads, college catalogs, school announcements, articles, books, and job bulletins, to name only a few. Also, we find increasingly that technical writing is mentioned as a profession in news items, radio and television utterances, introductions of many kinds, and biographical sketches. It has even made the society page and obituary column.

Technical publications for government, industrial, educational, or public use run into a staggering annual total and represent the labor of a great many writers and editors. The subject matter ranges from rigorous theoretical studies to limited practical applications, and the approach from scholarly to casual.

The growth potential of technical writing is encouraging. We may logically expect that the profession will burgeon in direct proportion to our expanding technology.

1.1 NATURE OF TECHNICAL WRITING

As a type of nonfiction, technical writing usually may be classified as exposition (explaining, defining) or description (representing, analyzing). Seldom does it incorporate the other two classifications of nonfiction: narration and argumentation. The topics for technical writing come from engineering or applied science, distinguishing it from general nonfiction, which draws its material from nontechnical matters, and scientific writing, which draws its material from pure science.

In order to keep things in the proper perspective, the distinction should be made at the outset that technical writing serves technology, not the other way around. That is, technical articles, books, papers, and reports record and communicate the work and thoughts of engineers and applied scientists. This does not mean that a technical paper may not suggest or motivate — only that the basic role of technical writing is that of enlightened manservant rather

1

than master. This holds true even when one writes about his own technical work. In that case, he becomes the technologist who motivates himself the writer.

If writing is to serve technology faithfully, it must be clear, to be easily understood; factual, to preserve the accuracy of the subject; objective, to remain unbiased; logical, to make sense; and restrained, to preserve dignity. The style of good technical writing is usually consciously simple; a complicated writing style can obstruct understanding of a complex technical subject. Some practice is understandably required for mastery of these particulars. Technical writing, unlike imaginative literature, strives for concreteness, avoiding connotations and implications. This does not mean that the technical writer is devoid of imagination. He does indeed have imagination, but he uses it to visualize the subject clearly and to work out the most effective way of presenting it.

1.2 BACKGROUND OF TECHNICAL WRITING

Some laymen seem to think that technical writing is a new phenomenon. Apparently, the reason for this mistaken idea is the great flurry of report writing during and following World War II. But the truth is that technical writing has been around for several centuries.

Its actual beginning is lost in the past, but technical writing quite possibly originated with the first literate ancient man who had to render to his lord an account of the latter's lands or buildings, or had to record for colleagues or apprentices instructions in the art of boat building, mine digging, or tomb erection. Professor Miller has cited Vitruvius, architect to Augustus Caesar in 27 B.C., as the first historically important technical writer[1], but the story goes further back than that. The biblical accounts giving the dimensions of Noah's ark and of the ark of the covenant are fragments of technical writing. Down through the ages, as fortifications and other structures became more numerous and complicated, and as man devised machines, the need to write about them increased. Chaucer's *A Treatise on the Astrolabe* (complete with illustrative examples), a set of simple instructions on the use of that predecessor of the sextant and thought to have been compiled around 1391, may be regarded as one of the earliest technical instruction manuals in the English language. With the development of science and industry in the sixteenth, seventeenth, eighteenth, and nineteenth centuries, technical writing grew steadily. In the twentieth century, it has attained professional status. The all-out world-wide efforts in armament development and space exploration since about 1940 have generated tons of technical literature.

[1] Walter James Miller, "What Can the Technical Writer of the Past Teach the Technical Writer of Today?" *I.R.E. Transactions on Engineering Writing and Speech*, EWS-4, No. 3, December 1961.

1.3 TYPES OF TECHNICAL LITERATURE

The technical writer has a broad field in which to exercise his talents. The literature of engineering and applied science includes compositions of many types: abstracts, articles, books, brochures, descriptions, handbooks, instructions, journals, lessons, letters, magazines, manuals, memoranda, monographs, pamphlets, papers, proposals, reports, specifications, and treatises. In addition, advertisements, surveys, patents, and résumés sometimes require the technical writer's professional attention.

These various technical compositions differ widely in format, and indeed a single type may vary noticeably when written to satisfy the requirements of different publications or companies. However, all technical writings exhibit in common the writer's attention to the attributes discussed in Section 1.1.

Of the various compositions listed above, only the technical report is the concern of this book.

1.4 LEVELS OF TECHNICAL WRITING

Unlike a literary work, a technical composition must be addressed to a specific audience. This is usually easy, for most technical writing is generated by a need for information. In this respect, every technical composition is "solicited"; the technical writer does not enjoy the luxury of writing, as some poets do, for himself alone. He must anticipate his audience. Knowing its needs, status, education, experience, and probable questions — at least approximately — he then must write in a manner appropriate to that audience, that is, intelligibly, without talking down or talking up.

The good technical writer thus fits his writing to the reader's level. His aim is to communicate the subject matter with accuracy, clarity, and fidelity, without dullness — never solely to impress. He would not aim highly complex mathematical material, for example, at a reader whose training ended with high school algebra. Nor would he belabor an obvious point for a qualified reader.

There are many ways to divide technical writing according to level. One is to separate it first into the categories of *theoretical* and *practical,* and then to divide each of these categories into *advanced, intermediate,* and *elementary:*

> I. *Theoretical*
>   A. Advanced
>   1. Graduate engineers
>   2. Advanced engineering students

    B. Intermediate
       1. Junior engineers
       2. Senior technicians
    C. Elementary
       1. Technicians
       2. Amateurs

II. *Practical*
    A. Advanced
       1. Senior technicians
       2. Advanced amateurs
    B. Intermediate
       1. Technicians
       2. Amateurs
    C. Elementary
       1. Beginning technicians
       2. Beginning amateurs
       3. General laymen (owners of equipment, nontechnical personnel, and so on)

The reasonable professional level of readers is shown in each of the categories in the foregoing list. However, such a separation must recognize that some crossing of the lines is possible. For example, a self-educated engineer or a senior technician might possibly comprehend material written at the advanced theoretical level, but in that case the responsibility is his, not the writer's. Each reader group is able, of course, to understand material written at any lower level.

The listing above accommodates all types of technical compositions, from the complex, scholarly paper or highly technical report (IA, advanced theoretical) to the simple instruction sheet for operating a home appliance or the article in a hobbyist magazine (IIC, elementary practical).

1.5 WHO DOES THE WRITING?

The engineer who does the research very often does the writing. After completing a technical project, he then must write a report or article describing or explaining it. This is especially true in the case of new engineers. The portion of the engineer's time devoted to technical writing has been placed at various figures between ten and fifty percent. The situation is a divergent one. One fact is agreed upon, however, and it is that the young engineer's advancement in his organization depends as much upon his ability to communicate effectively as upon his technical proficiency.

But the engineer is not the only one who writes in industry. Companies that can afford it employ technical writers who assume the full load. In fact, a highly stratified company is apt to have a full-scale publications department staffed by technical writers, editors, typists, and illustrators. Some technical writers gather material from the engineers and assemble it into professional papers or reports; others double as temporary engineers or technicians, working on a project and simultaneously recording the material which they will later write up. The existence of a technical writing staff within the company he plans to join, however, should not decide the engineering major against developing his own writing competence. He will have ample opportunity to profit from this tool.

1.6   QUALIFICATIONS OF THE TECHNICAL WRITER

First of all, the writer needs a strong background in English grammar and composition. Technical writing, as well as literary writing, is enhanced by good grammar, correct spelling, standard punctuation, strong sentences, and good paragraphs (the engineering student should give as careful attention to his English as to his mathematics). The technical writer must also be up to date on preferred writing practices, usages, and forms and should be able to compose rapidly. Additionally, he should be reasonably skilled in use of the typewriter or dictating machine.

But that is not all. The technical writer also must know what he is talking about; he must be familiar with the engineering field in which he works or he will be either tongue-tied or erratic. This means that he must either be an engineer or have acquired enough engineering knowledge to be competent. Only a few companies can afford the luxury of writers who merely polish the English of engineers. And those who can soon discover that such writers often unwittingly change technical meanings when they make syntactical changes.

The successful technical writer is enough of a realist to expect no perfect first drafts, even when he writes them himself. He therefore has the patience to rewrite a composition as many times as may be necessary to polish it.

1.7   TECHNICAL STYLE

The term *style* denotes the total effect of all the factors which distinguish one person's writing from another's. A particular way of writing may have been consciously adopted or accidentally acquired. In any case, the writing itself is grammatically correct. Thus, different writers on the same subject may express themselves quite differently while still using good English. This is made possible by the variety in acceptable English syntax.

Writing style embodies so many elements, some of them elusively subjective, that isolating certain ones is difficult. The mechanical elements that are readily revealed by analysis, however, include choice of words, word length, choice of sentence pattern, choice of word order, sentence length, degree of punctuation, order of clauses, and bulk. A few of the familiar nonmechanical elements arising as overtones of the mechanics are listed below. Some of these will be recognized as good, some bad, and some good or bad depending upon the writer's task.

ambiguity	complexity	gracefulness	pedantry
authority	concreteness	heaviness	shiftiness
brashness	condescension	honesty	simplicity
brevity	confusion	indirection	smoothness
brightness	directness	involvement	terseness
carelessness	dullness	lightness	vagueness
clarity	ease	logic	vulgarity
clumsiness	flippancy	obscenity	wordiness

Technical writing is not so rigid as to deny the writer any choice of style whatever. Nevertheless, it does not afford the greater freedom enjoyed by literary writers. For instance, the technical writer deals with a serious subject, so he makes no attempt to be amusing; still, he is not compelled to use only those words that cast a somber tone over any sentence in which they appear. But he would not use words that, either by secondary definition or connotation, are humorous. He is completely free to select the sentence form he judges most suitable for the occasion. For example, this sentence might thwart his efforts to secure a new appropriation:

> The new equipment will cost $100,000 and
> will boost our output by 50 percent.

A prudent writer would not hazard his cause by placing a shocking sum of money in the leading clause; instead, he would describe the fruits of the expenditure first:

> Our production will be increased a full 50 percent
> by the new equipment, which will cost only $100,000.

Since there are many levels of technical writing (see Section 1.4), a single writing style obviously cannot suit the entire field. The technical writer accordingly adjusts his style to the situation. This brings to mind the quality of *appropriateness*, which is an essential ingredient of any technical style; the style should be appropriate to the type of composition and to the intended audience. A writer uses a different style when preparing a paper for the journal of an engineering society than when writing an article for a popular magazine. Yet nothing is wrong with either of these styles; each is appropriate to its own situation. It certainly would be appropriate to write for the advanced reader that the area of Finland is 130,165 square miles, but it would probably mean more to the magazine reader if he were told that Finland is a bit smaller than the state of California. Similarly, the professional will want to know that each unit at New Jersey's first nuclear utility power plant, Oyster Creek, is expected to have an ultimate minimum capacity of 600 megawatts. But the lay reader probably cannot even visualize 600 million watts and will commend the writer who tells him that just one day's output of that kind of power would be the same amount of energy needed to operate his portable electric heater continuously for one year.

Because there are many kinds of technical compositions (see Section 1.3), one writing style could not suit all of them. Again, appropriateness is the deciding factor. An appropriate style for a freshman textbook would be unsuitable in a graduate text, just as a suitable magazine style would be out of place in a formal report. In general, as we move down the list given in Section 1.4, progressively more of the material must be spelled out for the reader. Consider this illustration: A description of the Wien-bridge frequency-sensitive network, for example, might be written this way at the elementary theoretical level:

> The Wien bridge circuit is shown in Figure 5-3. One arm contains resistor R_1 the second arm, resistor R_2; the third arm, capacitor C_1 and variable resistor R_3 in parallel; and the fourth arm, capacitor C_2 and variable resistor R_4 in series. This circuit has the peculiarity that it can be balanced for only one frequency (f) at a time. At null
>
> $$f = \frac{1}{2\pi\sqrt{C_1 C_2 R_3 R_4}}.$$
>
> If the resistance of R_2 is twice that of R_1, the balance equation is greatly simplified if R_3 and R_4 are ganged for simultaneous tuning so that $R_3 = R_4$ at all settings, and the two capacitances are equal: $f = 1/(2\pi\,C_1 R_3)$.

At the intermediate theoretical level, this might be reduced to:

> The Wien bridge circuit (Figure 5-3) contains two resistance arms (R_1, R_2) and two impedance arms ($C_1 R_3$, $C_2 R_4$). R_2 is twice R_1. The single null frequency is
>
> $$f = \frac{1}{2\pi\sqrt{C_1 C_2 R_3 R_4}}$$
>
> If $C_1 = C_2$, and R_3 and R_4 are equal and ganged, $f = 1/(2\pi C_1 R_3)$.

At the advanced theoretical level, most of the explanatory prose is super-fluous, and the description might be reduced still further to:

In the Wien bridge (Figure 5-3), $C_1 = C_2$, and $R_2 = 2R_1$. The single null frequency is

$$f = \frac{1}{2\pi\sqrt{C_1 C_2 R_3 R_4}}$$

Ganged, $R_3 = R_4$, and f becomes $1/(2\pi C_1 R_3)$.

Besides appropriateness, the following aspects of style are esteemed in technical writing.

Aspect	Description	How Achieved
Brevity	Shortness, compactness of statement. A long clear statement is superior, however, to a brief fuzzy one.	Short words, phrases, sentences, paragraphs.
Concreteness	Saying what is meant in a way that minimizes misreading.	Avoiding abstract nouns, vague sentences, and euphemisms.
Consistency	Writer's use of English and of technical terms conforms to current accepted practice and is unchanging throughout the work.	Using words and terms in a uniform manner.
Decorum	Good taste, propriety. The technical writer is neither a vulgarian nor a court jester.	Avoiding slang, profanity, dispensable shop terms, and substandard English.
Directness	Coming to the point quickly and definitely without deviation; not beating around the bush.	Avoiding circumlocutions and digressions.
Fluency	Writer's facility with grammar, composition, spelling, vocabulary.	Correct spelling, good grammar, accepted usages, clear sentences, and the best vord for the job.
Freshness	The flavor of newness, individuality. (The dullness of some technical writing results from its staleness.)	Avoiding clichés. Refusing to imitate cute, well-known current style traits.

Aspect	*Description*	*How Achieved*
Impersonality	Detachment of writer from text. The writer makes no attempt to enter the discussion or to identify himself with the reader. Exception: when the writer is required to accept blame or credit for what is said, and impersonality would imply evasion of the responsibility.	Avoiding first-person pronouns. Using verbs in the passive voice.
Logic	Good sense in what is said. Conclusions that naturally follow from the evidence presented. Recommendations that are justified by the conclusions.	Suiting a sentence to its sense. Avoiding a dependent clause to express a situation that is not dependent. Close use of parallel structures to express parallel thoughts.
Modesty	Absence of conceit or vanity, without subservience or self-depreciation.	Avoiding first-person pronouns, except where necessary to show acceptance of blame or responsibility. Using passive voice of verbs. Avoiding bold, unsupported assertions.
Naturalness	Freedom from artificiality. (This does not always mean "writing like you talk," since the quality of the writer's speech might be unacceptable.)	Avoiding the false elegance of high-sounding language. Avoiding classical allusions, unessential foreign words, stilted constructions, and bookish diction.
Positive language	Language using the positive form of the verb, which tends to remove the psychologically unpleasant aura of defeat that often surrounds a negative statement.	Substituting whenever feasible what *is* for what *is not*. Thus, "The satellite *put* a weak signal into Cape Kennedy," instead of "The satellite *did not put* a strong signal into Cape Kennedy."
Precision	Accurate use of language and of technical matter.	Meticulous attention to English mechanics and to close correspondence of language to technical fact.

Aspect	Description	How Achieved
Restraint	Holding emotions in check, dealing with the subject matter calmly, withholding personal bias, avoiding exaggeration.	Avoiding words and larger structures that have emotional connotations. Avoiding, where possible, words and phrases that imply a value judgment (*good, bad, unreliable, inferior*). Avoiding exclamations and superlatives.
Simplicity	Freedom from complication. (Understanding of a complicated engineering subject can be impeded by unnecessarily complicated language.)	Avoiding unessential long words and complicated sentences, rambling constructions, the use of a phrase where a word would do, foreign terms where English ones are available, and mathematics where plain English will do.

Good technical style avoids attracting undue attention to itself. This allows the reader to concentrate on the subject matter. The distracting effect of a conspicuous style is comparable to that of a loud noise or garish color. Good technical writing therefore is never flowery, seldom uses metaphors or farfetched similes, and rejects cute turns. It respects literally the rule that no writer should intrude between the reader and the page. Effective communication is the ultimate achievement of good technical style.

1.8   PROPERTIES OF TECHNICAL WRITING

Certain qualities distinguish good technical writing. Like traits of style, they are numerous and some are vague, but many can readily be identified and some of these are listed below. Stylistic devices in column 3 of the list are explained in Section 1.7. The other properties in column 3 are described elsewhere in this same list.

Property	Description	How Achieved
Authority	Dependable guidance through superior knowledge. Writer knows what he is talking about. The composition inspires confidence on part of reader.	By supporting every assertion and conclusion. Attention to stylistic concreteness, directness, logic, positive language, and precision.

Property	*Description*	*How Achieved*
Clarity	Clear presentation. Writing is easily understood. The meaning is usually grasped on first reading.	Stylistic brevity, concreteness, directness, naturalness, precision, and simplicity.
Coherence	Logical togetherness of the material. All parts of the composition hang together.	Effective use of transitions. Avoiding careless digressions. Attention to stylistic consistency and logic.
Completeness	The composition is a finished product. No portion of the writing task has been shirked or shortchanged. Completeness extends down to individual sentences.	Careful finishing of each part; stern inspection of final draft for missing items. Avoiding sentence fragments.
Confidence	Unobtrusive sureness on the part of the writer.	Avoiding unneeded hedging and qualifying. Attention to stylistic concreteness, consistency, directness, fluency, modesty, positive language, restraint, and simplicity.
Control	Constraint of the presentation within the bounds of professional integrity. The composition neither expresses the emotions of the writer nor appeals to those of the reader.	Avoiding exaggeration and unnecessary understatement. Attention to stylistic decorum, modesty, and restraint.
Dignity	A blend of composure and self-respect. A dignified composition reflects the dignity of the technical profession it serves, and exhibits respect for the reader.	Attention to stylistic authority, directness, fluency, freshness, impersonality, logic, modesty, naturalness, precision, and restraint.
Direction	Planned movement toward a clear goal. The good composition knows where it is headed and goes there.	Using a good outline. Working for completeness, organization, and unity. Informing the reader in advance what is to be covered.

Property	Description	How Achieved
Ethicality	Evidence of moral responsibility.	Strict conformance to the mores and rules of the technical and writing professions. Attention to stylistic decorum, precision, and restraint.
Fidelity	Faithful performance. The composition fulfills every detail of its implied contract with the reader.	Working for completeness, direction, finish, organization, selectivity, and unity. Attention to stylistic consistency and logic.
Finish	The state of final polish. The work bears the stamp of the professional.	Making repeated revisions and corrections until perfection is closely approached. Working for coherence, completeness, control, dignity, direction, and fidelity.
Objectivity	A detached, impartial point of view.	Writing in the manner of a disinterested (but not uninterested) second party. Attention to stylistic impersonality, modesty, and restraint.
Organization	Orderly and logical structure of the composition.	By careful planning, use of a good outline. Working for completeness, direction, and unity.
Reader-pointedness	Writing exclusively for the reader.	Accurate knowledge of the intended reader's comprehension level, experience, needs, and training.
Selectivity	Retention only of relevant material, and distinction between levels of importance in retained material.	Emphasis of principal material and de-emphasis of subordinate material by means of ascending order, descending order, typography (boldface, capitals, italics), displayed matter, headings and subheadings numbering, or tabulation.

Property	Description	How Achieved
Seriousness	Close, thoughtful concern, minus frivolity.	Strict attention to the topic under discussion, avoiding levity and superficialities. Working for dignity. Attention to stylistic concreteness, decorum, logic, modesty, precision, restraint, and simplicity.
Tact	The capacity to act as required while giving no offense.	Avoiding, where possible, direct or implied accusation, depreciation, reprimand, or ridicule. Assuming a courteous attitude and choosing language which runs little, if any, risk of offending even obliquely. Working for dignity. Attention to stylistic decorum, fluency, impersonality, and restraint.
Unity	Correspondence of all parts to the whole and to each other.	Discarding of any item that bears no important relation to the subject. Avoiding digressions.
Veracity	Truthfulness. Truth is the soul of science. Good technical writing never misleads or misrepresents.	Sticking to facts. Refusing to indulge in evasion, equivocation, quibbling, splitting hairs, or shifting the issue. Attention to stylistic concreteness, consistency, directness, fluency, logic, naturalness, modesty, positive language, precision, restraint, and simplicity.

1.9 THE TECHNICAL REPORT

A technical report is an account, usually in detail, of some matter such as (1) work completed or in progress; (2) findings from an investigation, information search, or study; (3) solution to a problem; or (4) offerings of specific theoretical or practical data. Like articles, books, and other technical compositions, it draws its subject matter from engineering and allied fields.

Reports are essential to the orderly conduct of affairs in industry, government, and education: The student writes a report describing a laboratory experiment he has performed, a manufacturing firm submits a progress report to a government agency from which it holds a contract, the head of a factory laboratory sends a report to his chief engineer giving performance data on a competitive product, a private consulting engineer reports to his client on the feasibility of using modular construction in an upcoming project.

When the objective of a work project is the development of an instrument or machine, the hardware is sent to the client along with a final report. But when the project is concerned with research, design, or study, a report usually is the only tangible item that emerges from the program. In such a case, the client is especially justified in demanding a professionally prepared document. To be sure, he wants sound technical work, but for his $150,000 outlay he also expects something better than a freshman term paper.

Technical reports vary in length from a single-page letter (see Appendix 3) to several books (see frontispiece). They are prepared by a single writer or by a staff of persons, and the time required for their production varies from a few minutes to several years. The technical writer in industry spends most of his time writing reports, and much less time on other technical compositions.

There are many kinds of reports. According to their nature, they may be classified as *formal* and *informal;* according to frequency of issue, as *monthly*, *quarterly, semiannual, annual* or *final*; according to type, as *laboratory, study, informational, recommendation, performance* (of a device), *test, work progress, or survey;* according to occurrence as *regular* or *interim;* and according to state as *normal* or *emergency.* These are the principal kinds. The list might be extended endlessly if we tried to account for every special technical need.

The technical report conforms to all of the standards of good technical writing, especially the particulars described in Sections 1.7 and 1.8. It differs from an article or paper primarily in format and terseness. (The structure of the report is described next in this book.) In addition to obeying general rules, the technical report writer sometimes must follow a prescribed organizational plan and structural details dictated by his company's stylebook or by the agency which contracts his company (for example, military specifications).

EXERCISES

1.1 Select in a current technical journal an article on a subject that you understand very well. Rate the effectiveness of the writing in the following manner: In answer to each of the following questions, write 10 for always, 8 for often, 5 for sometimes, and 0 for never.

(*a*) Does the writer seem faithful to the journal reader?
(*b*) Is the writing simple?

(*c*) Is the writing clear?

(*d*) Is the writing consistent?

(*e*) Is the language natural?

(*f*) Is the composition coherent?

(*g*) Are the statements concrete?

(*h*) Does the author get to the point quickly?

(*i*) Does the author develop his topics logically?

(*i*) Does the composition have precision?

1.2 Write a 500-word discussion of a laboratory experiment you have performed, and use a completely objective (impersonal) style.

1.3 In the following passage, which is typical of novice writing, the sentences are almost isolated. Rewrite the passage to give it coherence.

Gases are usually collected over water. They are collected in a pneumatic trough. One form of trough is shown in the accompanying sketch. The bottle that is to be filled with gas is first filled with water. It is covered with a piece of filter paper placed over its mouth. Then it is set mouth downward on the platform of the pneumatic trough. The trough has been previously filled with water just above the platform. Then the paper is removed. The gas is brought into the trough through a tube inserted under the platform. The gas bubbles through the water up into the bottle and replaces the water that it forces out.

1.4 The following paragraph contains inconsistencies in writing: shifts between active and passive voice of verbs, between personal and impersonal style, between one form and another of technical terms, and between indicative and imperative mood of verbs. Rewrite the paragraph to remove these inconsistencies.

The volume coefficient of expansion for a material is given as the change in volume per unit volume/degree centigrade change in temperature. We give the coefficient of expansion (linear) as the change in length per unit length per °C change in temperature. Using standard tables, find the coefficient of linear expansion of fused quartz, and you should find the coefficient of volume expansion of H_2O.

1.5 Poor spelling is one evidence of inexpertness in writing. Rewrite correctly the following words, which are misspelled as they often appear in technical compositions.

alloted	diaphram	heigth	noticable
auxilary	embarass	indispensible	paralell
changable	equiptment	maintainence	repellant
cieling	exagerrate	neccesitate	supercede
comparitive	fullfil	nickle	visability

1.6 Punctuation helps the technical writer to pinpoint meaning. Full punctuation is favored (over open punctuation) because it leaves little doubt as to the writer's intentions. Fully punctuate the following sentence.

The temperature at which this thin film evaporation is carried out is 5°K measured as close as practicable to the substrate pressures of 10^{-10} torr or lower may be reached with the equipment shown.

1.7 Engineering writing sometimes is condemned for unnecessary devotion to such phrases as "it would appear that," "it is obvious that," "it can be shown mathematically that," and to such redundancies as "microscopically small," "large in size," "green in color," "mathematical number," and "period of time." Select in a current technical journal an article that you understand very well and list all such words and phrases which, in your opinion, the author uses superfluously.

1.8 Simplify the following first-draft sentence by removing all deadwood and if necessary, using more than one sentence.

It is a fact that as long as a force is trying to speed up a machine (of whatever sort), it has to overcome both the friction — another way of thinking of resistance — and a certain opposition, always present, to the building up of speed, which is what we call inertia.

1.9 Using good technical style, write a 1000-word essay explaining why avoidable shop talk and other technical jargon is inappropriate in technical writing. Show, for example, what words you would substitute for terms like *dingus*, *gadget*, *gimmick*, *gismo*, *juice*, *mike*, and *scope*, as they are used informally in your major technical field.

1.10 A quack doctor, aided by two radio experimenters, has constructed a preposterous machine which he claims can diagnose every kind of disease. He plans to mass produce the machine and wants you to write a handbook, including a convincing theoretical explanation of the machine, a copy of which will be sent to each buyer. From what Section 1.8 says about ethicality, would you feel free to accept his assignment? Explain in a 500-word essay, using good technical style.

2

Anatomy of the Technical Report

A well-organized report is divided into easily recognizable parts arranged in an effectual sequence. From usage, these parts have become standardized, and are used as required in an individual report. Because reports are of different types and have diverse objectives, they might not be structured exactly alike. However, a study of a large number of reports will show that all of them have certain parts in common and that most effective writers, whether free-acting or stylebook committed, arrange these parts in approximately the same sequence.

Structural details of the principal types of reports — formal, informal, and laboratory — are discussed in this chapter.

2.1 FORMAL REPORT

A. Definition. A formal report is a full-scale, detailed, tightly structured document. Always dealing with some highly serious matter, it is sedate both in tone and appearance. It usually is long but does not have to be. The formal report is always assumed to be a permanent record.

B. Parts of the Formal Report. A formal report may contain the following parts, arranged for effective communication in the report, in the sequence shown in the following master list:

> *Front Matter*
> Title
> Cover
> Title page
> Letter of transmittal
> Approvals
> Distribution (circulation) list
> Preface
> Acknowledgments or credits
> Table of contents

> List of illustrations
> Abstract
> Summary
> *Main Text*
> Introduction
> Discussion
> Conclusions
> Recommendations
> *Back Matter*
> Appendixes or addenda
> Glossary
> Bibliography or list of references
> Index

The first twelve parts, from title to summary, are termed collectively *front matter* (that is, material in the front of the report, preceding the main text), the next four parts *main text* (that is, the report proper), and the last four parts *back matter* (that is, material in the back of the book, following the main text). It is quite possible that some of these parts may be omitted from a particular report simply because they are not needed. For example, one or more of the following parts especially might be missing: letter of transmittal, approvals, distribution list, acknowledgments or credits, list of illustrations, abstract or summary (but never both), appendixes or addenda, glossary, bibliography or list of references, index. The others, however, are deemed essential. Occasionally, the table of contents is omitted, but only when it appears certain that since the divisions of the particular report are few, the reader can get quickly to parts of it without a table of contents. Notice that the specimen student report (Appendix 2) is a formal report, yet it contains only

> Title page
> Letter of transmittal
> Table of contents
> Summary
> Introduction
> Discussion
> Conclusions
> Recommendations
> List of references

It required none of the parts it omits from the master list. Note that the professional report (Appendix 4) contains only

> Title
> Cover

Abstract
Introduction
Discussion
(all of the text material on report pages
2–21)
Conclusion
Acknowledgment
References
Addenda

C. Description of the Parts. The following discussions explain briefly the nature, role, and characteristics of the parts of the formal report.

1. *Title.* The title is a word or phrase that states the subject of the report. Since it is the first part of any report that is read by a person searching for information, a title should contain everything needed to give a truthful description of the report, nothing more and nothing less. Because of this requirement, it would be wrong to say that a title must always be brief: The title *Vibration Analysis*, for example, is misleadingly brief for a report that could not hope to cover such a broad field in its entirety, but the title *Controllable Vibration in the XRE-16 Helicopter* is accurate though longer. Some titles are short enough to be written on one line; others require two or more lines.

A title may be unitary (that is, complete in itself like the two given in the preceding paragraph) or multiple (that is, consisting of a main title and subtitle). Some multiple titles have elements on separate lines, especially when the subtitle denotes a particular phase of a subject identified by the main title:

FEASIBILITY STUDY OF THE PDP-5 DIGITAL COMPUTER
Use of the PDP-5 as Pulse-height Analyzer in
Gamma-ray Energy Spectra Analysis

Others combine the two parts, with colon punctuation, especially when the subtitle serves only to amplify the main title:

ATTENUATION OF HIGH-INTENSITY MICROWAVE
FIELDS: FERRITE METHOD

Since a title is the most succinct digest of a report, the final composition of it should be postponed until the report is completed and the writer can see what is *really* dealt with. In some instances, however, the title is predetermined (for example, *Third Quarterly Progress Report on Development of Test Equipment, Contract NX-401*).

In a title written in capital and lower-case letters, only the principal words have initial capitals. An article, conjunction, or preposition has a lower-case initial letter unless it stands first in the title. See, for illustration, the article *the* in the following titles:

Performance of the Gas Chromatometer

The 30-MP Gas Chromatometer

The title appears on the cover and title page. In some reports, it also appears at the top of the first main text page (see page 1 of the specimen student report in Appendix 2).

2. *Cover.* Most long formal reports are bound. The outside front cover displays these elements:

> Title and subtitle
> Contract or job name and number
> Date of issue
> Report number
> Serial number
> Copy number

The front cover of a particular report may contain as many of these items as required. In addition, some covers carry the author's name and job title, the classification notice (*confidential, secret,* or *top secret* printed conspicuously at the top and bottom of the cover), and the agency or client for which the report was written.

The inside back cover and outside back cover generally are blank, but the inside front cover sometimes carries approval notices. Note that the front cover of the professional report in Appendix 4 carries the following elements, from top to bottom: company report (paper) number; title of report; author's name, section name, company name, division name, and official address; name of agency to which presented; date; and company identification.

A cover should be informative, legible, and attractive. Some companies design a new cover for each report; others settle on a distinctive cover (sometimes displaying the company insignia or a tasteful illustration) and use this cover for all reports simply by changing the information it carries. Most formal report covers are either white or of some single, soft, neutral color. A few, however, use two or more colors chosen by, or in consultation with, graphic artists. Some reports use a window-type front cover, that is, one with a rectangular cutout which displays the title and a small amount of other information printed on the title page underneath. This type of cover usually contains only the company name and address and can be used with any report.

3. *Title Page.* The title page is usually the first right-hand page of the report. It contains all of the information that appears on the front cover. Additionally, it may carry one or more of the items (such as serial number and copy number) that generally appear on the front cover but in this case are put inside the report. The title page should be informative, symmetrical, and uncrowded. Illustrations, other than company insignia, usually are withheld from it.

In some reports, especially those which are inexpensively produced or have no need of the protection afforded by covers, the title page serves as the front cover. This is true of the specimen student report in Appendix 2.

4. *Letter of Transmittal.* A letter of transmittal is addressed to the primary recipient of the report, and serves to identify the report and formally present it to the recipient. The letter should carry the date of issue of the report, must be signed by whoever is responsible for the generation and transmission of the report, and it should contain the following information: title of the report; contract, work, or project number; number of copies of the report accompanying the letter; and distribution (names and addresses of all parties other than the primary recipient to whom reports have been sent, and the number of copies sent to each). The letter of transmittal is reproduced in each copy of the report.

See the letter of transmittal in the student report in Appendix 2.

5. *Approvals.* Often, a report must be read and approved by one or more officials before it may be issued. The authorities may be officials in the organization issuing the report, or military or naval dignitaries of the district in which the reporting organization is located. Each such person's name and title (and any other customary identification) must be given and his signature reproduced above his printed or typed name.

Approvals generally are placed on a separate page, especially if there are many of them. If there are only a few, they sometimes are placed on the title page.

6. *Distribution.* The primary recipient of a report must be informed of who besides himself has received a copy of the report. This is not only ethical, but actually required by some contracts, particularly government contracts. For this purpose, all recipients are identified in a distribution list, also called a circulation list.

The name of each recipient must be given together with his official title, company or agency name, location (unless well known), number of copies sent to him, and copy number of each report sent to him, as required. When the distribution list is long, a separate page is provided for it; otherwise, it appears on the title page.

7. *Preface.* The preface offers the report to the reader. It states briefly and clearly the subject and purpose of the report, its intended scope, its relation to other reports in the program, by whom the work project and report

writing were authorized, and whether this report is final or one of a series. If the author's name is prohibited on the front cover or title page, it might be given here. So might the names of persons who have helped, if there is no separate acknowledgments page. Note that the preface introduces the report, not the subject matter (introducing the subject is the role of the introduction).

Although laymen often interchange the words *preface* and *foreword*, discriminating writers and editors recognize a formal difference between the two. Specifically, a preface is written by the author, whereas a foreword customarily is written by a second party, usually an expert in the field served by the report, and can contain praise which modesty forbids from the author.

8. *Acknowledgments or Credits*. The ethics of science and of writing demand that credit be given where it is due. The writer therefore diligently names each person and each organization that has contributed to the work program or to the report that describes it. Sometimes the nature of the contribution is also described. Permission must be obtained for the use of previously published material, and this permission must be acknowledged. These citations are made on a separate acknowledgments or credits page when the names are numerous; otherwise, they are made in the preface or introduction, whichever seems most appropriate.

Acknowledgments should be made briefly and tastefully. Expressions intended to be witty sometimes fall flat on the printed page.

9. *Table of Contents*. This table lists in sequence the material appearing in the report. Each of its entries contains the name of the topic and the number of the page on which discussion of it begins.

The table of contents must contain every major topic appearing in the report, but nothing that is not clearly identified by heading or subheading in the report. See the table of contents of this book and of the specimen student report (Appendix 2).

The table of contents can be prepared only when the manuscript is in final form and paged. However, a good topical outline, faithfully followed, automatically provides a ready-made list of topics, needing only the page numbers to become a table of contents.

10. *List of Illustrations*. When there are ten or more illustrations, it is helpful to the reader if a separate "table of contents" is prepared for them. This list of illustrations must identify each illustration and give the number of the page on which it appears. Some reports having a great many illustrations of several kinds provide separate lists of diagrams, photographs, and maps, and also of charts and tables.

A long list of illustrations should be a separate part of the front matter. If the list is short, however, it may be run at the end of the table of contents.

11. *Abstract or Summary*. Laymen tend to regard *abstract* and *summary* as different names for the same piece of writing. But discriminating writers and editors recognize a distinct difference between the two. Since they are

confused so often, however, the two are considered together here, in order that their differences may gain clearness from closeness.

The basic distinction is one of function: An abstract *discusses* the report, whereas a summary *digests* it. Thus, an abstract gives a quick answer to "What is the report about?" while a summary gives an equally quick answer to "What does the report say?" For illustration, examine the student report in Appendix 2. This report has a summary on its page *iv* which, in eleven lines, digests twelve report pages. The substance of the report is contained in this summary. An abstract of the same report might read like this:

> The report discusses varistor action in an inexpensive, forward-biased germanium diode (Type 1N34A). Average test data are given for 100 diodes, and formulas are offered for calculation of forward resistance. Advantages and disadvantages are both discussed, and recommendations are made for further studies.

Note that this abstract makes no condensation of the report (as the summary does) but talks about it. See also the abstract on page *i* of the professional report in Appendix 4.

Abstracts and summaries serve two different classes of reader. Both want to know something about a report without reading it through or even scanning it. But the reader who needs a summary wants to know substance, and the one who needs an abstract wants to know coverage. Some writers, unsure of the exact needs of the audience and wishing to supply both types of reader, play it safe by providing separate abstracts and summaries. Others work for compactness by providing what is known as an *abstract and summary*, a piece that contains elements of both. The following passage is an example of the latter based upon the student report in Appendix 2. Here, the summary-type sentences are italicized; all others are abstract-type. It is incomplete but serves to illustrate the form of the abstract-and-summary.

> This report discusses varistor action in an inexpensive germanium diode. *Tests on 100 Type 1N34A diodes show that a resistance change of 600 to 1 can be obtained by varying the diode forward current from 1 microampere to 30 milliamperes.* Practical applications of this simple action are considered. *They include tuning, modulation, amplitude stabilization, tube or transistor biasing, and voltage regulation.*

As indicated in the master list (see Section 2.1B, the recommended position of abstract, summary, or abstract-and-summary is ahead of the main text of the report. The reader expects to find it in that place and should not be compelled to thumb through the report. However, some reports do place the summary at the end.

The abstract, summary, or abstract-and-summary should be written only after the rest of the report has been completed, and should be written as briefly as possible while still retaining accuracy and clarity. No rule of thumb, such as a 200-word minimum, is practicable in every case. Usually, a separate page is reserved for this passage but occasionally it may be found at the top of the first main-text page in a short report.

12. *Introduction.* This is the first part of the main text of the report. The purpose of the introduction is to present the subject of the report initially to the reader. Note that it does not present the report itself — that is the role of the preface. It has often been said that the introduction can "make or break" a piece of technical writing. This certainly seems true when we consider that good writing in the introduction can kindle the reader's interest in the subject and make him want to get on into the report proper.

There is no set formula for writing an introduction, because each subject requires individual treatment. But some of the items that should be present (though not all of them have to be in every introduction) include:

1. Identification of client

2. Identification of general subject (for example, electric blowers)

3. Identification of specific phase of subject covered by report (for example, development of a cryogenic destratification fan)

4. Historical background
     (*a*) of subject
     (*b*) of reporter's experience with subject

5. Technical background
     (*a*) General theory (underlying general subject)
     (*b*) Specific theory (underlying reporter's work and findings)
     (*c*) Description of reporter's work program
     (*d*) State of the art before and after contributions by reporter

6. Work status
     (*a*) Work completed
     (*b*) Work remaining

7. Credits for aid and special services rendered and for permissions granted, unless these already appear in acknowledgments or preface.

Although a certain amount of overlap is inevitable, the introduction should avoid invading the territory of the abstract and summary.

13. *Discussion.* This part describes and explains the main business of the report. If the document is a progress report, for example, the discussion explains the nature, objective, and results of work completed up to the end of the reporting period; if the document is an investigative report, the dis-

cussion reviews the conduct and findings of the investigation. Tests and experiments are described here, as are also observations, advantages, disadvantages, and methods used to collect data and make measurements and analyses.

Data are included in the discussion unless they are so numerous as to impede the reading without significantly contributing to the explanations. Large collections of data are better placed in appendixes and referenced, by means of footnotes or parenthetical statements, in the discussion. Virtually all of the illustrations appear in the discussion section. Note in the specimen professional report (Appendix 4) that the discussion (untitled as such, but easily recognized) fills most of the report, extending from page 2 to "Conclusion" on page 21. In the specimen student report (Appendix 2), the discussion is titled and extends from page 3 to "Conclusions" on page 10.

The discussion must be written clearly and completely, with close attention paid to the details of good technical writing given in Sections 1.7 and 1.8. There is no watertight formula for writing a good discussion. It is worth noting, however, that many report writers have found advantage in using what has been called the "backward order," that is, giving a brief summary of the results first and then describing the work. Such a sequence is immensely helpful to the busy reader, because it answers at once his most urgent question: "What finally happened?" His subsequent reading into the discussion fills in the details.

14. *Conclusions.* Next to wanting to know the results of work performed, the report reader wants to know their significance: "What is the meaning of it all?" He should not be forced to draw conclusions from his own analysis of the data; the report must do this for him in the section titled *Conclusions.*

Conclusions need not always be affirmative. But they must always be logical; that is, each one must be adequately supported by evidence presented in the discussion, and must reasonably arise from a consideration of such evidence. Unsupported conclusions are inadmissible.

Conclusions should be stated clearly and accurately and in decreasing order of importance. If there are many of them, they should be presented in such a manner that the knowledgeable reader can distinguish between the first-order (primary) conclusions and second-order (secondary) ones. Only primary conclusions should be repeated in the summary. Note that the specimen student report (Appendix 2) contains only primary conclusions (pages 10, 11) and that all of these are therefore carried over into the summary (page *iv*).

The term *conclusion* is sometimes used, in another sense than the one in which it has been used here, to mean "final remarks," and designates that section of a composition that consolidates the main points in a terminal statement. This is the kind of conclusion that appears on page 21 of the specimen professional report (Appendix 4).

15. *Recommendations.* After studying the conclusions, the reader will next want to know what should be done as a result of the reported work. In view of this, the report should clearly propose, in the recommendations section, whatever further action is suitable. This action may be either affirmative or negative, as logic determines.

Recommendations must be supported by conclusions. It is illogical, for example, to recommend that a certain design change be made if the conclusions have already shown that it has no merit. Recommendations for additional work often need no direct support from the conclusions, provided the reasons for the work are stated or are obvious to a knowledgeable reader.

Recommendations, like conclusions, should be listed in decreasing order of urgency. First-order (primary) recommendations should be easily distinguishable from second-order (secondary) ones. Only first-order recommendations should be repeated in the summary.

16. *Appendixes or Addenda.* All important supplementary material that would be obstructive in the main text of the report should be placed in the appendix. Such material includes charts, tables, illustrations, letters, sample documents, and lengthy mathematical derivations. There may be several of these back-of-report sections, each appropriately numbered or lettered (see the appendixes of this book).

The appendix is not a catch-all; no material should be placed in it that properly belongs elsewhere in the report. Neither should interesting but unessential material be appended merely to swell the report.

An addendum may contain the same kind of material that is placed in an appendix, and there may be several addenda appropriately numbered or lettered. Sometimes *addendum* and *appendix* are used interchangeably. But the addendum usually contains material which has in fact been added, as when new or missed material is attached in a second printing.

Appendixes or addenda are listed in the table of contents (see the table of contents of this book).

17. *Glossary.* A glossary is a brief dictionary of special terms used in a report or important in understanding it. It should give a compact and lucid definition of each such term and where necessary an example of its use. Standard, familiar terms should be avoided unless they are used in some special way in the report.

Glossary entries are arranged alphabetically and usually are listed in only one way (thus, *air-speed indicator* but not *indicator, air-speed*). The following is an example of glossary entries:

Specific gravity
The ratio of the density of a substance to that of water.

Specific heat
The amount of heat required to change the temperature of a unit

mass of a substance 1 degree. It is expressed in cal/gm°C or Btu/1b°F.

Specific inductive capacity
(*See* Dielectric constant)

18. *Bibliography or List of References.* The bibliography and list of references both contain information regarding published or unpublished works that were consulted during the work program or preparation of the report, or that are recommended to the reader for further study.

The entries in a bibliography are listed alphabetically by last name of the senior author, which is written in inverted order (the name of an additional author appears in the normal order, that is, first name first). The following form is recommended for data, order, and punctuation:

Mace, Arthur E., *Sample Size Determination.* New York: Reinhold Publishing Corporation, 1964.

Schwartz, S., ed., *Selected Semiconductor Circuits Handbook.* New York: John Wiley & Sons, Inc., 1960.

Wilcox, Glade, and Charles H. Butler, *Industrial Calculating Devices.* New York: Holt, Rinehart and Winston, Inc., 1962.

Bibliography entries are generally unnumbered.

In a conventional list of references, the works are listed in the order in which they have been first cited in the report, not in alphabetical order, and they are numbered accordingly:

1. Stuhlinger, Ernst. *Ion Propulsion for Space Flight.* New York: McGraw-Hill Book Company, Inc., 1964.

2. Chalmers, Bruce. *Energy.* New York: Academic Press, Inc., 1964.

3. Horn, Louis J. "Be Practical About Your Printing," *Consulting Engineer*, June 1964, p. 104.

In the main text of the report, a work is cited by means of a number in parentheses. Thus, the first work is indicated by (1), the second by (2), and so on, generally placed at the end of a sentence:

Horn states that "if small press runs are involved, zinc halftones would serve just as well as the long wearing copper halftones" (3). (This number refers to item 3 in the list of references — see above.)

A particular work may be referenced as often as necessary throughout the report. Its number simply is repeated. Thus, in the foregoing example, (3) always refers to the article by Horn.

See for illustration the list of references in the specimen student report (Appendix 2) and the citations of the works on pages 1, 5, and 11 of that report.

19. *Index.* If a report is very long, its table of contents may prove insufficiently detailed as a quick guide to desired material. Such a report should be provided with an index, which offers a great many more page-identified listings than is possible with a table of contents and, being alphabetized and cross-referenced, permits quick location of a topic.

The index can be made only after the writing and paging of the final draft of the report are completed. The indexer carefully reads the final draft and makes out a 3 in. $\times$ 5 in. index card for each topic. On this card is noted a *single* topic and the page on which it appears. The topic is cross-indexed on separate cards:

Silicon carbide, 569

                             Crystals
                                silicon carbide, 569

Silicon compounds
    carbide, 569

After the reading is completed, the cards may be arranged alphabetically and the index written directly from them. See, for illustration, the index of this book.

D. Language of the Formal Report. The language of this type of report is strictly formal. The chief characteristics of formal language are:

1. Complete sentences
2. Acceptable usages
3. Mature vocabulary
4. Attention to parallelism
5. Lack of affectation
6. Freedom from avoidable jargon (*ball-park* value, *gimmick, gremlin, jigger, slipstick*)
7. Avoidance of substandard terms (*iuice, movie, talkie*)
8. Avoidance of contractions (*can't, don't, I'll, you've*)
9. Avoidance of clipped words and terms (*hi-fi, phone, scope*)
10. Good grammar
11. Correct spelling
12. Full punctuation

2.2 INFORMAL REPORT

A. Definition. Some technical matters may be communicated quite simply in short documents which have no need of the extensive structural detail of the formal report. This is particularly true of short subjects and of interim reporting. Such information is transmitted adequately by the informal report, which is usually in the form of a letter or memorandum.

B. General Parts of the Informal Report. Because of its brevity and simplicity, the informal report requires fewer divisions and sections than the formal report (Section 2.1B), but it does retain the principal parts of the formal report:

> Title
> Approvals
> Distribution
> Summary
> Introduction
> Discussion
> Conclusions
> Recommendations

It sometimes also contains an appendix and/or bibliography and it may be illustrated. Some parts, such as approvals, distribution, and recommendations, are omitted from a particular report if they are unnecessary.

The parts are almost never labeled as such, but are clearly discernible. For example, in the specimen letter report in Appendix 3, paragraph 1 is the introduction, paragraph 2 the summary and discussion, paragraph 3 the conclusions, and paragraph 4 the recommendations.

C. Parts of the Letter. The principal parts of a letter are (1) heading, (2) date, (3) inside address, (4) salutation, (5) body, (6) complimentary close, (7) organization name, (8) written signature, (9) typed signature, (10) title of signer, and (11) identification symbol. Additionally, the letter may have certain auxiliary elements: (12) attention line, (13) reference line, (14) subject line, (15) attachment or enclosure notice, and (16) distribution notice. These parts are labeled with the same numbers in the sample letter report shown in Figure 2-1. The various parts are discussed separately below.

1. *Heading.* This part appears at the top of the first page. It contains the sender's name and address and any additional information deemed necessary. The heading is printed on the letterhead and does not have to be written except when a makeshift letterhead is improvised.

The complete address should appear in the heading (that is, street address, city name, state name, and postal zip code number) unless the sender is so well known locally that a street address is unnecessary. State names should be used unless the city is extremely well known (for example, Boston,

SONIC MEASUREMENTS LABORATORY, INC.

2010 Dedham Parkway

Denver, Colorado 80205   ①

②

July 7, 1964

⑬ Ref: Your letter of
        May 29, 1964

⑭ Subject: Type 341 Pre-
        amplifier

Strato Aircraft Company
③ 85 Langley Street
Los Angeles, California 90045

⑫ Atten: Mr. John Low, Service Superintendent

④ Gentlemen:

Measurements have been completed on the Type 341 Preamplifier you submitted for evaluation, and this letter reports our findings.

Test results show the performance of this amplifier to be
well within the limits suggested by you; namely, minimum
overall voltage gain, 100; distortion less than 0.25%; frequency response, $\pm$ 1 db from 20 to 20,000 cps; and hum
⑤ level better than -50 db.

The following repeatable test data were obtained:

OVERALL VOLTAGE GAIN: 150 at 1 kc (gain control at
                                      maximum)
HARMONIC DISTORTION: 0.06% max (see attached Curve
                                      A)
INTERMODULATION DISTORTION: 0.05% (60 and 7000
                                      cps comb.)
FREQUENCY RESPONSE: $\pm$ 0.3 db 10-25,000 cps (see
                                      attached Curve B)
HUM AND NOISE: Better than -65 db
INPUT IMPEDANCE: 2 meg shunted by 20 pf

Fig. 2-1 Specimen Letter Report

The Type 341 appears to be satisfactory for use as a general-purpose audio-frequency preamplifier for shop-type instrumentation and test purposes such as you suggested to us.

We recommend the Type 341 Preamplifier for use in the trouble-shooting section of your aircraft maintenance shop.

Please let us know if you will require further test data.

⑥ Very truly yours,

SONIC MEASUREMENTS LABORATORY, INC. ⑦

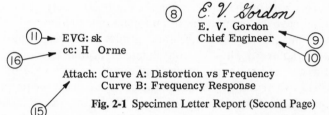

⑧ *E. V. Gordon*
E. V. Gordon

⑪► EVG: sk   Chief Engineer ◄ ⑨
⑯►   cc: H Orme   ⑩

Attach: Curve A: Distortion vs Frequency
          Curve B: Frequency Response

⑮

Fig. 2-1 Specimen Letter Report (Second Page)

Chicago, New York City), and the state name should be spelled out, where practicable, for added surety.

Some highly stratified organizations provide separate letterheads for their various units, and the headings of such letterheads carry, in addition to name and address, the name of the unit (for example, Department, Division, Laboratory).

2. *Date.* The full date on which the letter is written (for example, September 10, 1963 or 10 September 1963) is placed on a separate line and punctuated as shown here. Do not use month abbreviations (Sept. 10, 1963) or numerical dates (9/10/63).

3. *Inside Address.* This address is called "inside" because it appears on the letter inside the envelope; the same information appearing on the envelope is called the "outside address." The inside address contains the name of the addressee and his complete address (street number, city name, state name, and postal zip code number). Ordinarily, a letter report is addressed to an organization (see Figure 2-1). But occasionally it is addressed to an individual. In that case, the organization name is preceded by his name (with his title if it is customarily used in his organization, or if there is more than one person by the same name there):

Mr. J. P. Jones
Eastern Computer Products, Inc.
2100 Baxter Road
White Plains, N. Y. 10604

In a large organization, delivery may be slowed unless an addressee's location is given in detail:

> Mr. H. Brainard Fancher, General Manager
> Semiconductor Products Dept.
> General Electric Company
> Electronics Park
> Syracuse, New York 13201

Notice that no end punctuation is used in the inside address. The only end periods in the two preceding examples are those that follow abbreviations.

4. *Salutation.* This part of the letter greets the addressee. Several forms are available and all have in common the colon as end punctuation.

The salutation must agree in number and gender with the addressee named in the inside address. Thus, if Consolidated Vacuum Corporation has been named as the addressee, the proper salutation would be "Gentlemen" or "Dear Sirs"; whereas if Mr. John Smith has been named, the proper salutation is "Dear Sir," "Dear Mr. Smith," or "My dear Mr. Smith." The salutation must also match the tone of the letter and gravity of the business; an intimate salutation, for example, would be out of place in a letter dealing with an impersonal matter discussed with an addressee scarcely known to the writer. The following salutations are listed in decreasing order of formality:

Sir:	Madam:
My dear Sir:	My dear Madam;
My dear Mr. Smith:	My dear Mrs. Smith:
Dear Sir:	Dear Madam:
Dear Mr. Smith:	Dear Mrs. Smith:
Dear John:	Dear Mary:

"Ladies" or "Mesdames" is proper when the addressed organization is known to be composed of women only; "Gentlemen" is used when the organization is headed by both men and women. The masculine plural salutation "Gentlemen" is the most common in letter reports and letters of communication.

A personal salutation ("Sir," "My dear Mr. Smith," and so on) is used only when a person's name appears in the inside address — not when the letter is merely called to an individual's attention (as in the attention line, (12) in Figure 2-1).

5. *Body.* The body is the text of the letter and is equivalent to the main text of the formal report. The body should have clearly recognizable, though unlabeled, parts: introduction, summary, discussion, conclusions, and

recommendations. In addition to these elements, a well-structured letter has a termination, usually a single line, which avoids leaving the reader abruptly. These parts may be identified in the specimen letter given in Figure 2-1: paragraph 1, introduction; paragraph 2, summary; paragraph 3, discussion, paragraph 4, conclusions; paragraph 5, recommendations; and paragraph 6, termination. They may be identified also in the specimen letter report in Appendix 3.

6. *Complimentary Close.* The complimentary close is a farewell phrase which, though somewhat archaic in form and occasionally deceitful in manner, is considered a necessary courtesy to the addressee. It precedes and introduces the signature and is always end-punctuated with a comma.

The modern formal complimentary close is based upon the adverbs *cordially, respectfully, sincerely,* or *truly,* and it may consist of this word only or some combination of the chosen adverb plus the modifier *most* or *very* and/or the possessive pronoun *yours,* in the normal or inverted order. There are 33 acceptable forms of the complimentary close, ranging from the almost curt "Yours" to the pretentious and slightly suspect "Most sincerely yours." The one chosen by a writer must match the salutation *and* the subject of the letter. For instance, the friendly complimentary close "Cordially" is inappropriate for use with the stiffly formal salutation "Sir," and the same is true of the formal "Respectfully" with the intimate "Dear Frank." "Yours truly," "Very truly yours," and "Yours very truly" are the most widely serviceable complimentary closes in formal letters.

Appropriateness and sincerity should underlie the choice of any complimentary close. "Respectfully," for example, is appropriate for those addressees, such as authorities and dignitaries, who merit the writer's respect, "Sincerely" should be reserved for those situations in which the integrity of the writer and reported material is to be assured, and "Cordially" is permissible only when there is established friendliness between addressee and writer.

7. *Organization Name.* The name of the organization issuing the letter follows immediately the complimentary close and is typed in full capitals. This is the same name that appears in the heading. This element is omitted only when the signer operates a business or practices a profession under his own name.

8. *Written Signature.* The written signature of the writer of the letter (or of the official authorized to sign it) appears next after the organization name.

9. *Typed Signature.* The name of the signer of the letter is typewritten immediately under the handwritten signature. This is a safeguard against the possible inability of the recipient to decipher the handwriting.

10. *Title of Signer.* The signer's official title (such as Chief Engineer, Director of Research, President, Foreman) appears under his typed name if

use of titles is customary in his organization or is required by the addressed client. Sometimes, the signer's department, division, section, or group is named along with his title (for example, Design Group, Missile Section, St. Louis Division).

11. *Identification Symbol.* This is a combination of the writer's initials in full capitals and the typist's initials in lower-case letters. The two groups of initials are separated by means of a colon (:) or solidus (/). When the writer does his own typing, the letters *ms* (abbreviation for *manuscript*) are substituted for the typist's initials.

12. *Attention Line.* This line calls the letter to the attention of an individual in the addressee's organization known by the writer to have authority over the matter dealt with by the letter. This usually insures that the letter will be routed quickly to the responsible party. The presence of a name in an attention line, however, does not alter the salutation; the person would not be named in the salutation.

13. *Reference Line.* By naming the request, authorization, or inquiry that prompted the letter, this line saves much searching of memory or files by the addressee

14. *Subject Line.* Here, state briefly and accurately the subject of the letter. The subject line is a courtesy to the addressee and an invaluable aid to file personnel and others both in the sending and receiving organizations: it allows any reader to determine preliminarily what the letter contains and to decide if the matter concerns him. Thus, the subject line is comparable to the title of a formal report.

15. *Attachment or Enclosure Notice.* When supplementary material is attached to, or enclosed in, a letter, this fact should be signaled by means of the word *attachment* or *enclosure* (or the abbreviation *attach* or *encl*). When there is more than one attachment or enclosure, each should be listed, as is done in the specimen letter in Figure 2-1. It is safe practice to use an enclosure notice even when the enclosed material has been mentioned earlier in the letter (as in paragraph 3 of the specimen letter).

This notice serves to remind clerical personnel at the sending end to enclose the material, and it alerts the addressee to the fact that supplementary material should be found in the letter.

16. *Distribution Notice.* It is ethical to apprise the addressee of all other recipients of the letter. This is done by listing their names after the symbol *cc*: which is the abbreviation for copy (or copies). If there is a chance that a recipient may be unknown to the addressee, his brief address or professional affiliation (company, government agency, university) should be given with his name (for example, Paul G. Burke, Universal Tank Co.).

D. Parts of the Memorandum. When used for informal reporting, the memorandum is usually confined to the sender's own organization, although it is occasionally sent to an outsider. It deals with its subject less formally even than the letter; consequently it needs fewer parts than any other type of report. For example, it has no salutation, complimentary close, or typed name. The parts of the memorandum are heading, date, reference line, to line, from line, subject line, body, signature, identification symbol, distribution notice, and attachment or enclosure notice. (When necessary, a bibliography or list of references is included in the memorandum.) These parts are discussed individually below. A specimen memorandum is shown in Figure 2-2, and its parts are coded for identification with the same numbers used in this discussion. A sample memorandum-type report is shown in Appendix 1.

To save writing time, many organizations supply fill-in-type blanks for memoranda. These blanks are preprinted with a heading and the words *To, From, Date, Reference,* and *Subject,* and the writer needs only to fill in the appropriate information. In the preprinted blank, the sharp contrast between the printed words and the typed-in matter (see Appendix 1) provides adequate visual separation between the two, so no punctuation is required. This contrast is missing when the blank and the matter are both typewritten, so colons and white space (see Figure 2-2) must be used to separate parts titles from typed-in matter.

1. *Heading.* This is similar to the heading of the letter, but generally shows organization name without address. Some printed memorandum blanks even dispense with organization name and simply show the term "Interoffice Memorandum" as the heading.

2. *Date.* The full date on which the memorandum was issued appears here. Abbreviated dates (such as 2/7/63) are not good form.

3. *Reference Line.* Here is given a brief identification of the inquiry, order, or request (if any) that prompted the writing of the memorandum.

4. *To Line.* This element is equivalent to the inside address of the letter. It contains the addressee's name and also often either his title or location. It seldom contains a detailed address unless the organization is highly de-centralized; the location usually given is the addressee's department.

Greater informality is permissible here than in the letter. The addressee's name thus may appear in familiar form (*Jack Baker* instead of *John G. Baker*) and the location may be abbreviated (*Plant Engineering* instead of *Department of Plant Engineering*). In some intances, a first or last name alone is sufficient.

5. *From Line.* This line shows the sender's name, and it may also give his title or location. As in the "To" line, the location is seldom given in greater detail than the name of the sender's department unless the organization is so highly decentralized that the full address of the sender is needed.

As in the "To" line, greater informality is permissible here than in the letter. The sender's name may appear in familiar form (*Hank Stewart* instead of *Henry J. Stewart*) and his location may be abbreviated (*Test Lab*

①

AZTEC ENTERPRISES

①   INTEROFFICE MEMORANDUM

DATE: February 7, 1963   ②

③   REF: Your memo of
February 5, 1963

④   TO: A. L. Morris
Plant Engineering

⑤   FROM: Fred Small
Prototype Laboratory

⑥   SUBJECT: Power Drain of Laboratory Equipment

In response to your memo, we measured the power drain
of our laboratory equipment, exclusive of power used for
lighting only.

Here are the wattages at 115 volts a-c:

⑦

Test Instruments: 1600   All individual mea-
Power Tools: 1126   surements are
Soldering Irons: 1000   listed on the attached
Oven: 5000   data sheet.
Vacuum Pump: 248

TOTAL DRAIN: 8974 w

Please plan for twice this much power for our laboratory
at the new plant, since all of our equipment will be dupli-
cated after we move.

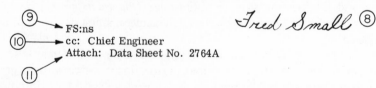

⑨   FS:ns
⑩   cc: Chief Engineer
     Attach: Data Sheet No. 2764A

⑪

Fred Small   ⑧

Fig. 2-2 Specimen Interoffice Memorandum

instead of *Test and Measurements Laboratory*). In some instances, a first or last name alone is sufficient.

6. *Subject Line.* Here the subject of the memorandum is stated accurately and as briefly as practicable. This line, like the subject line of the letter, is equivalent to the title in a formal report. It allows the addressee and file personnel to determine the contents of the memorandum preliminarily.

7. *Body.* The body of the memorandum, like that of the letter, is equivalent to the main text of the formal report. But the body of the memorandum might contain only a few of the five major report elements (summary, introduction, discussion, conclusions, recommendations), because it often has no need for all of them. Sometimes, for example, the memorandum merely transmits information and is required to draw no conclusions and make no recommendations. The body of the specimen memorandum in Figure 2-2 incorporates only an introduction (paragraph 1), discussion (paragraph 2), and recommendation (paragraph 3).

The discussion in the body should be as brief as practicable, and should contain only primary data and illustrations. Secondary data, calculations, and illustrations should be placed in an attachment. If the discussion and other elements require many pages for complete presentation and numerous subdivisions labeled to keep them straight, a formal report instead of a memorandum is indicated.

8. *Signature.* The handwritten signature of the sender gives official status to the memorandum and acknowledges the sender's responsibility for the contents. The additional typed name, required in the letter, is unnecessary in the memorandum, since the typed name already appears in the "From" line. Some organizations consider the sender's initials sufficient as a signature, and these initials are written at the end of the body or at the end of the typed name in the "From" line.

9. *Identification Symbol.* As in the letter, this symbol is composed of the signer's initials in full capitals and the typist's initials in lower-case letters, with a colon (:) or solidus (/) between the two groups of letters. If the signer does his own typing, the symbol *ms* (the abbreviation of *manuscript*) is substituted for the typist's initials.

10. *Distribution Notice.* Each recipient of the memorandum, other than the addressee, is listed here. His name is usually sufficient. But if two or more recipients have the same name, or if the recipient is outside of the organization, a department name (and sometimes company name and address) also is required.

11. *Attachment or Enclosure Notice.* This element identifies any material that may be attached to, or enclosed with, the memorandum. Such supplementary material includes blueprints, calculations, charts, clerical forms, graphs, illustrations, letters, mathematics, photocopies, tables, and test data.

E. Language of the Informal Report. Although the approach of the informal report is less ceremonious and the structure less complicated than that of the formal type, formal language is used. See Section 2.1D for the characteristics of formal language. The only exception is the more intimate address and identification permitted in the "To" line and "From" line (see Section 2.2D, parts 4 and 5).

2.3 LABORATORY REPORT

A. Definition. The laboratory report reveals data and findings from laboratory work, and serves, with the laboratory notebook, as the official record of such work. These reports issue in quantity from the laboratories of schools and industry. The material contained in the laboratory report is the basis of the discussion, conclusions, and recommendations in the formal and informal reports written later. A specimen laboratory report is given in Appendix 5.

B. Parts of the Laboratory Report. Various formats have been devised for laboratory reports, depending upon the specific requirements of different organizations. Generally, however, these reports contain the following elements: heading, report number, date, statement of object or purpose of test, description of apparatus used, description of procedure followed, observations, conclusions, and signature. These parts are discussed individually below and should be examined in the specimen report in Appendix 5.

1. *Heading.* A heading similar to that of the letterhead appears at the top of the first page of the report. Usually, this is nothing more than the title "Laboratory Test Report," but occasionally it contains the organization name and location, especially when the reports are sent outside of the organization.

2. *Report Number.* This is the serial number of the report and may indicate only the position of the report in a filing sequence. It enables quick recovery of the report and, along with the date, shows the position of the reported work (and the report itself) relative to other work in a sequence.

3. *Date.* The date line should show the date on which the report was officially issued. The unabbreviated form of the date is recommended (for example, January 9, 1961) but some organizations sanction a simple numerical date (for example, 1/9/61).

4. *Object.* This section describes clearly, but as briefly as practicable, the object or purpose of the reported work. It should be revised painstakingly to correct any ambiguity or vagueness.

5. *Apparatus.* All apparatus and equipment used in the performance of the work must be listed, except for commonplace components the use of which is taken for granted. When listing apparatus, give name of the equipment, manufacturer's name, model number, and serial or inventory number.

This information will enable other workers to set up the identical equipment if the test results subsequently must be checked. If a piece of equipment was custom designed and/or constructed by the reporter's own organization, it should be given an assigned model number with the organization's name, or it should be designated "composite," not "homemade."

6. *Procedure.* This is a complete chronological account of the work and is one of the rare appearances of narration in technical writing. The procedure section should describe the work accurately and fully, in a step-by-step manner, but as briefly and simply as practicable. To minimize ambiguity, full, rather than telegraphic, sentences should be used (for example, *The type A100 manometer was used to check the bypass pressure* rather than *A100 manometer used to check bypass pressure*).

Although some slight overlap is occasionally unavoidable, the procedure should avoid duplicating or overlapping observations and conclusions.

Illustrations are sometimes required in the procedure section. These are usually assembly or wiring diagrams, flow charts, and functional block diagrams.

7. *Observations.* Here are recounted the observations made while the work was performed. This is sometimes a narrative discussion. Oftener, it merely presents recorded data, and comments on their significance (as in the specimen laboratory report in Appendix 5).

Analyses and comparisons sometimes are found in the observations section, especially if the report is very short.

8. *Conclusions.* Like the same section in formal and informal reports, the conclusions here enumerate the facts that may reasonably be reached from a critical examination of the data. All conclusions must be supported by clear evidence given in the observations section. The conclusions section must be closely related to object (observe, for example, in the specimen laboratory report in Appendix 5 how the conclusions portion answers the question inherent in the object section).

9. *Signature.* A responsible person, usually the one who did the work and wrote the report, should sign the report to make it official and to establish responsibility for its contents. Sometimes this is a full signature. Often, however, handwritten or typed initials are accepted (as indicated by the technician's typed initials in the specimen laboratory report, Appendix 5).

10. *Additional Elements.* Other sections which appear in some laboratory reports include analysis, calculations, data, and recommendations. Separate sections are required for analyses and calculations when the latter are too numerous to be included in the procedure section, as they are in the report in Appendix 5, and for data when they are too numerous for the observations section. Recommendations are made only occasionally in laboratory reports.

C. Language of the Laboratory Report. Formal language is used in the laboratory report (see Section 2.1D for the characteristics of formal language). However, phrases often replace sentences in the object and apparatus sections (see Appendix 5).

EXERCISES

2.1 List the parts that are common to formal and informal reports.

2.2 Write a 1000-word (approximately) discussion explaining the differences among the abstract, the summary, and the abstract-and-summary. Give illustrative examples.

2.3 Write a 500-word (approximately) discussion explaining the difference between the bibliography and list of references. Give illustrative examples.

2.4 Select a laboratory test report that you have prepared in your major field. Using the information given in that report, prepare (*a*) a memorandum-type informal report for your department head, and (*b*) a letter-type informal report for the president of your company or college. (See Appendixes 1 and 3 for format and structure.)

2.5 Discuss the several conventions regarding the signature in (*a*) a letter, (*b*) a memorandum, (*c*) a laboratory report.

2.6 Account for the occasional use in the laboratory report of such additional sections as analyses, calculations, data, and recommendations.

2.7 Obtain a recent, formal, professional report. Identify each of its parts according to the list given in Section 2.1C. Which parts are not included in this report? In what way would the report have been more effective if these parts had been included?

2.8 Prepare a table showing the chronological order in which you think the parts of the formal report (Section 2.1C) should be written. Defend your sequence.

2.9 Your company is engaged in a developmental program as a subcontractor for the Wilson Corporation. This is the beginning of the seventh month of the one-year program and you recently submitted your second quarterly progress report. During the past week, your plant was demolished by fire, and you must report this matter to the Wilson Corporation. Which type of report do you consider appropriate for this purpose? Explain fully.

2.10 Explain why only first-order conclusions and first-order recommendations are permitted in the summary.

2.11 Select any three consecutive pages from Chapter 2 of this book and prepare an index for the material on these pages, following the procedural description given in Section 2.1C (part 19).

2.12 Write a 500-word foreword for this book, keeping in mind the difference between a preface and foreword (see Section 2.1C (part 7).

2.13 It is sometimes said that a short report is necessarily an informal one. Comment on the accuracy of this statement, keeping in mind both the similarities and dissimilarities between formal and informal reports as explained in this chapter.

2.14 The language of the letter report and memorandum report is usually formal, although these are informal reports. Explain fully the reason for this.

2.15 Write the appropriate complimentary close for each of the following salutations:

(*a*) Sir:
(*b*) Dear Sir:
(*c*) My dear Mr. Smith:
(*d*) Dear Jim:

2.16 Informal technical reports are sometimes addressed to dignitaries. Using a current edition of a dictionary or writer's handbook, find the correct salutation to be used for the following dignitaries:

Ambassador	Navy Commander
Army General	President of College
Associate Professor	Roman Catholic Cardinal
Chief of Police	State Senator
Clergyman (Protestant)	Superior Court Judge
Dean of College	Supreme Court Justice
Governor of State	U. S. Congressman
Mayor of City	U. S. Senator

2.17 For each of the dignitaries listed in Exercise 2.16, determine the correct form of address to be used in the inside address of a letter.

2.18 Explain why the following elements are required in a letter report: (*a*) organization name after complimentary close, (*b*) typed signature.

2.19 Explain the circumstances under which use of the recipient's job title is appropriate in the inside address of a letter report.

2.20 Explain why incomplete sentences are permissible in the object and apparatus sections of a laboratory report. Give illustrative examples.

3

General Procedures for Report Writing

Most report writing situations are highly individual, since few of them can share many features. They accordingly make different demands upon report writing. An effectively written report in one such situation may be unsuitable in another, and this prompts the corollary, dear to teachers and writers, that there is no best report but only many good ones.

A second corollary, closely related to the first, states that there is no best way to write a report but only many good ways. It recognizes that several writers may proceed quite differently in the way they write a given report and that the result will be satisfactory in each case. However, this applies to writing within individual parts of the report; there is good agreement on the steps, and the chronological order in which they are taken, in the over-all writing of a report.

These steps and related matters are introduced here and are discussed in detail in the following chapters.

3.1 STEPS IN WRITING

A time-proved good way to write a report is first to subdivide the job into essential steps, and then to complete the corresponding parts step by step. There are seven of these steps and they apply to all kinds of technical reports. Most report writers follow them in the order in which they are given here: preliminary planning, collecting material, making an outline, writing the rough draft, illustrating, revising and rewriting, and preparing the final report. The listing is chronological and includes all of the writing, not publishing, phases. Each of these steps is described in detail in a separate chapter following the present one, and they are introductorily defined below.

A. Preliminary Planning. This includes all designs and decisions as to the nature of the report and the schedule for its preparation. While this is not strictly a writing phase, it gives order and direction to the actual writing which follows.

42

B. Collecting Material. This also is not a specific writing phase, but it may contain a great deal of preliminary notes that will find their way into the report. The principal concern here is the gathering of the technical and supporting information that will be the subject matter of the report.

C. Making an Outline. With the material at hand, the writer can decide upon the best way of presenting it. At this point, he prepares an outline to crystallize the plan and to offer a guide for systematic development of the report.

D. Writing a Rough Draft. The writer, following his outline, writes the first, unpolished manuscript of the report.

E. Illustrating. If illustrations are required, they will have been selected or planned, at least preliminarily, in the preliminary planning and collecting material phases. Some illustrations will be in finished form at this stage. At any rate, the writer will be able to write about each illustration and will have before him rough sketches of those that are in process. Their exact positions will be decided as the last revisions are being written.

F. Revising and Rewriting. This is the correcting and rewriting of the original draft and succeeding ones as many times as are required to give the manuscript final authority and polish. This task sometimes is performed by writer only, editor only, or writer and editor.

G. Preparing the Final Report. This phase includes all the steps required to complete an acceptable final draft of the report, ready to be set in type by the printer or reproduced by a process other than printing.

3.2 METHOD OF WRITING

For accuracy, legibility, and neatness, all technical report manuscripts are typewritten. Some writers, however, prefer longhand for a rough draft, later transcribing the handwriting to typescript. Others favor a dictating machine. Still others find that they can compose satisfactorily with a typewriter. The selection should be made in accordance with the writer's own abilities, experience, and temperament. The best choice is the method that affords the individual writer maximum speed, least distraction, ease of correction, and good legibility. All revised drafts, however, *must* be typewritten in their final form — and a rough draft likewise must be typewritten when it is to be read by a second party. *Keep a copy of everything you write* and be sure that all carbon copies are clean and sharp.

All drafts must be retained intact for reference and comparison until some discreet date following publication of the report. If the report is classified (confidential, secret, top secret), the drafts may be destroyed only by, or under the supervision of, a security officer.

Good technical style should be used (see Sections 1.4, 1.7, and 1.8). However, language precision is the result, almost always, of careful revision

— time should not be wasted in concentration on mechanics and style in the rough draft.

Report writing follows a time schedule. The technical writer, unlike some literary artists, must write compulsorily. He cannot wait for inspiration or the "right mood." If he happens to be one of those geniuses to whom the right word or the correct structure flashes automatically, and from whose pen the sentences flow smoothly, well and good. But most often the technical writer is no such genius. Instead, he is a determined toiler to whom, as to Samuel Johnson, "Composition is, for the most part, an effort of slow diligence and steady perseverance." But his resolution frequently enables him to write circles around the desultory genius.

3.3   MANUSCRIPT MECHANICS

All drafts of the report manuscript should be clean and legible. The original rough draft will, of course, show signs of inferior English and of experimentation (erasures, cross-outs, insertions, and strikeovers), but a final version of this draft to be circulated for reading should be cleaned up.

Avoid pencil. A penciled manuscript is easily defaced and often hard to read. Use a nib-type pen for handwriting (only the very best ballpoints, which neither smear nor skip, are acceptable). But, better still, type the final version of each draft.

All drafts, whether handwritten or typed, must be line-spaced and provided with ample margins, for easy insertion of corrections, additions, and suggestions. Double-space the lines (triple-space between paragraphs); leave 1½ in. margins at the top and on the left and right sides of each page, and a 1 in. margin at the bottom. Indent the first line of each paragraph at least five spaces. Use plain white paper that erases cleanly.

For typescript, use a solid black ribbon and change it as soon as the impression begins to gray. Keep the type bars clean for a good sharp impression. Use a machine having pica type (this is the most common typewriter face), elite type (somewhat smaller than pica), or the letterpress type of some of the electric machines. Avoid special type faces, such as script, all capitals, slant letters, or square letters, which are available on some machines.

Number all pages clearly and consecutively with the page number in the same place on each page. (Exception: The first page of each chapter is numbered at the bottom in the final draft.) Number an inserted page with the number of the preceding page plus a letter of the alphabet (for example, a page inserted between page 5 and page 6 would be numbered 5A, a second page inserted here 5B, and so on).

3.4   NEED FOR APPROVAL

Various approvals (editor, engineering department, legal department, patent office, public relations, and so on) occasionally are required at different stages of report writing, and it is wise to secure them before proceeding to the next phase.

Often, a draft must be closely read and endorsed by a company official or military representative before it may be further processed. This invariably takes time, and still more time is consumed in the making of corrections, changes, and deletions before moving ahead. Where practicable, a check sheet, with a space for the signature or initials of each reader, should be attached to a circulating draft. When possible, separate copies of the draft should be sent simultaneously to the readers to save time.

3.5   REFERENCE TO GUIDES

The technical report writer needs standard, current reference material for guidance in the mechanics of writing. This is as essential a part of his professional equipment as his typewriter. The following books are recommended:

Webster's Seventh New Collegiate Dictionary. Springfield, Massachusetts, G. & C. Merriam Co., 1963.

Perrin, Porter G., *Writer's Guide and Index to English*, 3rd Ed. Chicago: Scott, Foresman and Co., 1959.

Roget's International Thesaurus, New Ed. New York: Thomas Y. Crowell Company, 1946.

Turner, Rufus P., *Grammar Review for Technical Writers.* New York: Holt, Rinehart and Winston, Inc., 1964.

United States Government Printing Office Style Manual, Rev. Ed. Washington: Government Printing Office, 1959.

An editorial office or publications department will, of course, have a copy of the unabridged dictionary.

In addition to the above books, the writer sometimes must have access to, and work from, military report-writing specifications or from a company stylebook. He will find it helpful also to have available a current glossary or dictionary of the technical profession which the report serves.

3.6 PROBLEMS OF TEAM WRITING

A great many reports are one-man products. But a respectable number are written jointly by two or more persons. The reason for group or team writing often is the simple requirement for division of labor — a team can do more work in a given time than a lone writer can. Moreover, the subject matter of a report may be so complex that a single writer will not be conversant with all of its technical aspects; hence, each writer in a group will concentrate on his own specialty.

Team writing introduces some problems. Chief matters of concern are coordination of member efforts (neither writer's work may lag so far behind the rest as to delay progress toward completion), duplication and overlap of material (a topic is usually discussed in only one place), unity of presentation (everything written should be related to the main subject), uniformity of style (the combination of the separate writings should appear to have been written by one craftsman). These problems generally are resolved by efficient administration. Thus the first three problems above can be put straight by good preliminary briefing and subsequent supervision by the editor or senior writer in charge; the last two can be promoted by having one person rewrite all of the separate contributions into a consolidated draft. Frequent team conferences are beneficial.

Team writing becomes difficult when there is little or no communication between members. This is apt to happen when members are cleared only at classification levels corresponding to the material they are assigned (for example, confidential, secret, top secret), and when members are employees of different companies preparing a joint report. In such instances, a competent liaison agent is needed.

EXERCISES

3.1 In an essay of approximately 1000 words, define and explain the seven steps in report writing.

3.2 During which of the seven steps in report writing is engineering supervision most needed? Explain fully.

3.3 From your own experience, compare the advantages and disadvantages of the following methods of writing a first draft: (*a*) longhand, (*b*) typewriter, (*c*) dictating machine.

3.4 The technical writer works when there is a job to be done, not when he is in the "right mood." Some critics have used the word "mechanical" pejoratively to describe this kind of writing. In approximately 500 words, explain whether in your opinion the quality of technical writing suffers or is untouched by this "lack of inspiration."

3.5 Why is it important to keep a copy of everything you write? If possible, use an illustrative example from your own experience.

3.6 List and describe the line spacing, paragraph indentation, and margin requirements for a manuscript page.

3.7 Select one of your own major-field term papers and write a 600-word critique of it in terms of Section 3.3 (*Manuscript Mechanics*).

3.8 Describe some of the new methods of correcting typewritten errors without ordinary erasing (correction paper, correction ribbon, paint-over, and so on), explaining their advantages and disadvantages. If possible, present for illustration a sample correction made with each method.

3.9 In approximately 500 words, explain how you would reduce overlap and duplication if you were supervising a three-man team writing a report on an exhaust-control device for automobiles.

3.10 Criticize the statement, "Aside from necessary science and engineering textbooks, the only reference work a technical writer needs is Webster's dictionary."

4

Preliminary Planning

The writing of a report proceeds more confidently and smoothly and stays under better control if all of the participants understand the nature of the desired end product, and know where they are headed and how far they have progressed toward completion at any instant. This calls for careful planning and scheduling at the outset. Some planning of this kind is always needed, even if it amounts to nothing more complicated than considering the best approach, structure, and tone before dictating a one-page letter report.

Preliminary planning is a flexible process, because it must be adjusted to suit an individual writing program. It has some requirements that are common to all situations, however, and these are listed in Section 4.1. One rule applies in every case: Preliminary planning should be completed before a single line of rough draft is written.

This planning phase is called *preliminary* because it is an initial step; its results are subject to modification as the writing progresses.

4.1 AIMS OF PLANNING

What type of report must be written, that is, will it be formal or informal? If it is to be informal, should the report be a letter or memorandum? How will the material be collected? What is the deadline for completion of the report? What then will be the deadline for completion of each part of the report? How will the report be reproduced — printing? Multilith? Xerox? mimeograph? other?

These questions and others like them concern matters that must be settled before the actual writing of a report is undertaken. There are still other matters that must be decided in individual cases. To go ahead without some settlement will result in many false starts, delays, and blunders. Know what kind of report is required, how and when the data for it will be supplied, and when each part of it must be completed. Plan each step in the writing process, and feel free to modify this preliminary plan (adding, deleting, and changing, as required) as the writing progresses.

Various aspects of preliminary planning common to all technical reports are discussed in the separate sections that follow.

4.2   SELECTING THE TYPE OF REPORT

This matter should be decided first. Obviously, the rest of the planning depends upon whether the report is to be formal, informal, or laboratory type, and if it is to be informal, whether it should be letter-type or memorandum-type. If the report is to be formal, decide which of the parts (Section 2.1C) will be required.

Sometimes the type of report is already prescribed. A formal quarterly progress report and an informal monthly report, for example, may be required by a government contract. In some instances when the type is not prescribed, this matter will be decided by management, with or without the advice of the writing staff. In each case, the writer would spend no time on this phase of preliminary planning but would simply make a notation as to the required type.

4.3   SELECTING A REPRODUCTION PROCESS FOR THE REPORT

More than one copy of the report most likely will be needed. How will it be reproduced? The answer to this question determines the nature of much of the work in the writing phases.

If the report is to be reproduced by letterpress printing, for example, a final manuscript must be prepared for submission to the printer, and halftones and line cuts will be required for illustrations; if it is to be reproduced by Multilith, the final draft and illustrations must be transcribed on paper or metal masters; if by mimeograph, the final draft and illustrations must be transcribed on stencils; and if by Ozalid or other "blueprinting" process, the final draft and drawings must be transcribed on vellum. If photocopying or Xerox is employed, the copy and illustrations will be reproduced directly from the final draft and illustrations.

Thus, the final manuscript will be handled in a different way for each such reproduction process, so the latter must be determined beforehand. Sometimes, the method of reproduction is prescribed in the contract under which the reported work is performed. When it is not prescribed, the method may be chosen by editors or management, with or without the aid of writers.

4.4   DETERMINING THE SOURCE OF MATERIAL

What will be the supply line of technical data for the report? Report material is obtained in two principal ways: (1) data are collected directly by the writer (that is, he is the engineer or technician who performs tests, investigations, or studies and records the data; he is the resident writer on a technical project, keeping a diary or journal to relieve technical personnel of the task; or he obtains the data by examination of laboratory notebooks and from conferences with technical personnel), or (2) the data are obtained by some other person or persons and delivered to the writer for processing. Sometimes, a combination of the two is employed.

Planning has to be different in each of these two cases. If the engineer does his own writing, he must plan to label data in his laboratory notebook and journal so that it can be located and interpreted quickly when he turns to the writing. If the writer is to "live with the project," keeping the diary or journal, an arrangement must be worked out for his participation and for his questioning of technical personnel. If the writer is to pick up data from notebooks and other documents, then he must be technically qualified to select and interpret what he finds, and arrangements must be made for his consultation with engineers, technicians, and other persons involved. Finally, if data are delivered to the writer, a schedule for such deliveries must be worked out to the understanding and agreement of all participants if deadlines are to be met.

4.5   SELECTING ILLUSTRATIONS

At this point in the report program, the writer and his colleagues have some idea as to the illustrations (line drawings, photographs, tables, charts) that will be needed. If not, the needs for illustration should be studied. These illustrations should be collected now if they already exist. And if they are not available, their preparation should now be assigned to illustrators and photographers, so that they will be completed when needed in the manuscript writing.

Where practicable, keep rough sketches of all artwork assigned to illustrators and of equipment setups scheduled for photographing. If this cannot be done, keep a brief description of such illustrative material, with each piece coded (either with the figure number expected to be used in the report, or some similar identification) for reference during writing.

It is difficult, of course, to make final decisions about illustrations at this preliminary point. Illustrations will be added, as the need arises, during the writing. But a nucleus of artwork is invaluable at this time. Experienced technical writers have observed that once the writer has illustrations at hand, he has something to talk about, and his writing goes much more easily.

4.6 ALLOWING FOR APPROVALS

Time must be allowed for the reading and endorsement of parts of the manuscript and of the entire final version of the report by officials, when this is required. When possible, set up a program, during the preliminary planning stage, for the reading of each part immediately after its completion. This will keep each reader aware of the date on which his services will be required and will reduce delays (see *Time Schedule*, Section 4.8).

4.7 PROVIDING FOR PUBLICATION

After the type of report is selected (Section 4.2), the planner decides the method of reproduction. The entire writing effort must then be aimed toward preparing a manuscript suitable for that method.

A portion of the planning must consider any additional work occasioned by reproduction if this work is to be performed by the writer. For example, letterpress printing entails the marking of copy for the printer and reading galley proofs and page proofs. This work may be done entirely by editors or aides, or it may be done wholly or partially by writers. If the writers must do it, then time for this nonwriting phase should be allocated during preliminary planning.

The setting up of reproduction schedules generally is handled by editors or management. It is attended to by the writer only when he is solely responsible for publication and must follow a report through from preliminary planning to bound copies.

4.8 PREPARING A TIME SCHEDULE

The first question to be answered here is "When is the report to be completed?" This date is the over-all deadline. The completion date depends upon the due date, that is, the date on which the report must be delivered at its destination. The farther the reporter is from the client, the earlier the completion date must be.

Once the completion date has been established, deadlines for the individual parts of the report can be set. These deadlines must be based upon an estimate of the length of each part of the report and the writer's speed. It is difficult to assess writing speed, since productivity varies with fatigue and other human factors, but every writer (and his supervisor) has some idea of his average daily output. Deadlines for the completion of illustrations must also be set at this point.

With the calendar as a guide and the report type and reproduction process already selected (Sections 4.2 and 4.3), the planner can prepare a reasonable time schedule. This schedule should show the date on which each part of the report must be completed if the over-all deadline is to be met, and its estimates are based upon the probable length of the part divided by the average daily output of the writer and the illustrators. For a report to be written from material supplied to the writer, the schedule might look like this:

1. Material to be received and checked: 5/1
2. Rough draft to be completed: 5/8
3. Illustrations to be received and finally approved: 5/11
4. Revisions and rewrites to be completed: 5/23
5. Final report to be completed: 6/15

This information is sometimes presented in a bar graph.

The schedule for writing a formal report lists the parts in the order in which they are normally written, not in the order in which they finally appear in the report. Thus the order would be: discussion, conclusions, recommendations, appendixes, glossary, bibliography, introduction, abstract or summary, preface, acknowledgments, table of contents, list of illustrations, distribution, approvals, index, letter of transmittal, title page, and cover. (Compare with the list showing order of sequence in the report — Section 2.1B).

EXERCISES

4.1 In response to a customer complaint, your company has tested the accuracy of 100 dial-type thermometers that you manufacture and that have been in dealers' stocks for over a year. The average error (in the 65–110°F range) was found to be less than ±1.5°F (your guaranteed accuracy is ±2 percent). Briefly show your preliminary planning for a letter-type informal report to the customer.

4.2 In approximately 1000 words, discuss the advantages and disadvantages, in your opinion, of the various ways of collecting report data discussed in Section 4.4.

4.3 Prepare a short memorandum (under today's date) to be attached as a check list to a circulating manuscript, advising the following readers of the reading requirement and date on which the manuscript with corrections must be returned to you: T. Burns, E. F. Karl, D. C. Richter, and H. Washington.

4.4 In what chronological order would you plan to write a short formal report that is to contain only the principal report parts? (See Section 2.2B for these principal parts.)

4.5 Prepare a sample time schedule, based upon an estimate of your own writing speed and drafting speed, for the specimen student report in Appendix 2. Assume that the experimental data will have been taken by an aide and that you will do only the writing.

5

Collecting Material

Factual material is the stuff of technical reports. It consists principally of data obtained through tests and measurements, investigations, studies, and surveys; observations and analyses of such data; calculations and predictions; and records of work completed. The report writer is responsible for gathering or receiving this material and casting much of it into readable prose. Although collecting material is largely a nonwriting phase of report production, the seeds of the writing are found here; and when the material is acquired through investigations, literature searches, and surveys, the writing itself often starts here.

Material may come to the writer in any one of several ways or through a combination of them. The following sections identify these channels and describe their functioning in relation to the technical report and its writer.

5.1 MATERIAL CHANNELS

There are two channels of supply: (1) the writer gathers material himself (primary acquisition), or (2) the material is gathered by someone else and turned over to him (secondary acquisition). In the former instance, the writer is a part of the reported work program; in the latter, his only function is to write the report.

Neither channel may fairly be declared superior to the other. Each introduces problems and imposes requirements. Primary acquisition, for example, requires that the writer be qualified in the technical profession served by the report and that he be proficient also in writing; but it insures that the writer is intimate with the program. Secondary acquisition presumes that the writer's full time is spent at his specialty and that he takes no part at all in the technical work, so it may necessitate a large amount of checking with, and watching by, the technical personnel.

The rules that apply are simple: (1) If you are worker (engineer, technician, investigator) as well as writer, remember that each piece of data, each bit of evidence that you acquire will be of potential use later on in the writing of the report. Record the material in a logical, systematic fashion so that you can write directly from it without having to solve puzzles, repeat experiments, or ask additional questions. When practicable, keep a journal, in addition to a laboratory notebook or investigation log. Make your entries clear enough to be expandable into units of the report later on. (2) If you are the writer only and receive the material from a second party, check it carefully, in consultation with him, to insure that it is complete and makes sense. (Some engineers are known to deliver to full-time technical writers miscellaneous notes in various forms ranging from paper scraps to complete notebooks. Such material should always be unscrambled, consolidated, and clarified immediately in close cooperation with the originator before it is incorporated into a draft.) (3) Make no technical change in material without the sanction of the originator. When you make a grammatical change, have the originator check the material to insure that the technical sense remains unchanged.

The various sources of material and the methods of collecting it, discussed separately in the following sections, all fall into one or the other of these categories.

5.2 LABORATORY OR FIELD WORK

Much of the material that goes into the reports of college and industry is obtained from laboratory and field tests and measurements (see Appendixes). The laboratory activity ranges all the way from simple experiments that demonstrate scientific principles to research into new methods and apparatus. The field activity similarly ranges from training exercises to original research and development.

If many tests are made, a large volume of data is accumulated. Not all of this is suitable for inclusion in a report; otherwise, the latter would become merely a reprint of the laboratory notebook. Unless there are instructions to the contrary, select the principal results that indicate trends or typical performance or that show specifics needed by the report reader. When all of the data must be carried over into the report, place only selected material in the discussion, and commit the great mass of supporting and supplementary data to an appendix. When the material is sparse, it may all be carried directly in the report. This has been done in the specimen reports shown in the Appendixes and in Figures 2-1 and 2-2.

Sometimes a portion of the laboratory work is done by the report writer, who works temporarily as an engineer or technician and records data and makes report notes as the work progresses. In such cases, management feels that in this way the writer becomes familiar with the reported work and needs less assistance during the writing phase, and also that the principal technical personnel are spared the additional task of preparing notes for the writer

(which they may do unsatisfactorily). In other instances, the writer is permitted to sit in on all of the laboratory operations and to keep a journal based
upon his own observations and upon answers to the questions he asks.
In the first case, where the writer is a participant in the technical work, he
must be either an engineer or technician himself; in the second case, where he
is an observer, the writer must either be an engineer or technician or possess
better than average informally acquired knowledge of the field.

If you keep a journal, enter into it a summary of the work performed on
the day of entry. State the results of the work and their significance, and
refer to laboratory notebook pages where supporting data or illustrative
examples may be found.

5.3 INVESTIGATIONS

There are many kinds of investigations, both technical and nontechnical.
The kind of interest here is the probing for information of any kind, which
involves the interviewing of people; examining of records; and/or inspection
of persons, places, or things. For example, a committee from the Major
Development Corporation investigates the technical capabilities of XYZ
Laboratories, Inc. and reports its findings to Major's board of directors.
The material the committee gathers for its report is obtained by interviewing
XYZ's engineers, scientists, and technicians; examining the company's
record of past performance (reports, articles, proposals); and inspecting its
physical plant.

There is no best way of conducting an investigation or of keeping its
records, since the circumstances vary with the large number of possible
investigations. But the general rules for the gathering of information apply
here: (1) record all data clearly, logically, and completely so as to present
little or no perplexity when a report is written from the record later on;
(2) make notations immediately so as to circumvent error in recall; (3)
transcribe tape-recorded material as soon as practicable; and (4) clearly
label photographs, sketches, maps, and other graphic exhibits.

The writer is sometimes also the investigator, and sometimes only the
recipient of material gathered by an investigator. When he is both, he must
be sufficiently well qualified in the field of the investigation to be able to
collect significant material and to comprehend it. Furthermore, if his information is obtained largely by means of interrogation, he should be a
proficient interviewer. If the writer takes no part in the investigation but re-
ceives the material and converts it into a report, he should inspect this material
in company with the originators to insure that he understands it. If he makes
grammatical changes, he should solicit an examination of the altered material
by the originators to insure that the sense remains unchanged. Sometimes,

the writer sits in on an investigation, taking notes and keeping a journal to relieve the investigators of this task and to accelerate production of the report.

5.4 SURVEYS

A survey may be defined as an act of comprehensive viewing. It is a procedure whereby information is obtained by analytically considering a quantity of conditions, elements, factors, items, or the like in an area, field, or group of interest. Thus, a survey of commercial ceramic materials would be conducted by means of inquiries and studies to ascertain (1) the names and types of ceramics; (2) where, by whom, and in what quantities they are produced; (3) their chemical and physical properties and production techniques; (4) their costs; and (5) their typical applications. The methods employed to gather this information would include interviews with manufacturers, sellers, and users of ceramics; studies of ceramics literature; and inspection of ceramic material production facilities and production of ceramic consumer devices.

The purpose of a survey is to uncover as much information as possible in a field of interest. Examples are a survey of the state of the art in semiconductors, a survey of electric power generation east of the Mississippi, a survey of commercial general-purpose digital computers, and a survey of glass cleaning methods in the mirror industry. In each case, the surveyors would inquire widely in the pertinent field to obtain the maximum amount of information and might submit the data subsequently to a statistical analyst. Sometimes a technical survey is related to human factors; for example, "Professional Status of Civil Engineers Ten Years After Graduation from Altavista University" would embody both technical and human factors.

As in investigations and laboratory or field work, the report writer may serve a dual function here; that is, he may also be a surveyor. Or he may function solely as a writer, receiving survey material previously collected by a survey specialist. However the material is obtained, it should be reasonably well organized — separated into the various categories of the report — to facilitate conversion into a report.

5.5 INTERVIEWS

Some of the material accumulated through investigations and surveys is obtained by interview. Some of the material resulting from laboratory and field work is obtained in the same way — by the report writer interviewing the technical people. There is no great mystery about the interview; it is common enough in our society. But there is considerable naiveté concerning its demands. Indeed, the common belief that interviewing is a simple task requiring a minimum of preparation is undoubtedly responsible for the ineffectuality of many interviews. A good interview must be carefully designed.

Basically, the interview consists of the asking of questions by the interviewer and the answering of them by the interviewee. But it is not confined to this form; the interviewee, for example, sometimes does all of the talking after being first prompted by the interviewer. Interviews may be classified as oral and written. The former entails direct interchange between participants, either face to face or by telecommunication, the latter the exchange of questions and answers in writing (letters, memoranda, questionnaires). The completeness and suitability of the answers in either case depends largely upon the aptness of the questions.

Only a few basic rules need be followed in effective interviewing:

1. Be courteous without being subservient.

2. Be brief. An interview often is an interruption; get all of the information you can in one installment.

3. Know the subject matter.

4. Reveal your motives at the start. The interviewee deserves to know the purpose of the interview and how you will use the information he supplies.

5. Frame your questions beforehand so that they will elicit the information you want. In an oral interview, you can rephrase the question whenever a reply is inadequate; but in a written interview, the question must work right the first time.

6. In an oral interview, record answers accurately. Avoid twisting, embellishing, or paraphrasing them.

7. Have the interviewee spell out any unclear matter and define any strange term.

8. Whenever practicable, let the interviewee see (or hear) your notes.

9. Be punctual. Start the interview on time and terminate it as soon as possible.

10. If you use a tape recorder, transcribe the material as soon as practicable.

In a written interview, do not use a printed questionnaire unless you are conducting a poll and this fact is clearly known to the interviewee. Instead, use an individually typed questionnaire.

The personal interviewer needs special qualifications not possessed by every report writer: a pleasant manner, the ability to listen well, quickwittedness, diplomacy, and a good sense of timing. In addition, he should be a master of shorthand or fast writing.

5.6 LITERATURE SEARCHES

What is sometimes signified by "research" is a search of literature — a careful reading of publications and notes on a topic of interest. Technologists and students are constantly making literature searches. The chemical engineer, for example, who is ordered to gather all of the information he can about polyester resins and submit an informational report on the subject, consults and takes notes from plastics journals, textbooks, encyclopedias, laboratory reports, and manufacturers' bulletins. Similarly, the student in search of material for a term paper on ceramic-to-metal seals takes notes from textbooks, articles, monographs, and encyclopedias available at the college library, and consults brochures and data sheets he obtains from manufacturers. A respectable amount of material in some reports (especially in the part of the introduction devoted to historical background) comes from literature searches.

Some writers use a notebook and others use cards for the recording of notes in a literature search. Cards offer the advantages of increased flexibility, ease of alphabetical arrangement, and ease of removal. Either 3 in. × 5 in., 4 in. × 6 in., or 5 in. × 8 in. cards may be used, depending upon the amount of information to be recorded on each. The following procedure will be found helpful:

1. Make a separate bibliography card for each book consulted. This card (see Figure 5-1) should contain (1) the library card catalog number of book, (2) the name of the author, (3) the title of the book, and

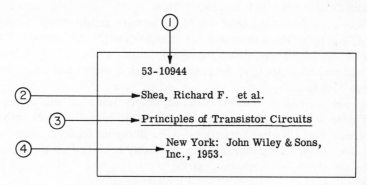

Fig. 5-1 Bibliography Card (Book)

(4) the facts of publication (city of publication, name of publisher, and year of publication). Later, on note cards, the book may be referred to briefly (as in Figure 5-3) by the author's last name and an abbreviated title.

2. Make a separate bibliography card for each article or paper consulted. This card (see Figure 5-2) should contain (1) the library card

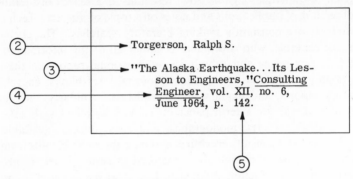

Fig. 5-2 Bibliography Card (Article)

catalog number (if any), (2) the author's name, (3) the title of the article, (4) the name of the journal or magazine in which the article appeared (together with volume, number, and date of publication), and (5) the number of the page on which the article begins. Later, on note cards, the article may be referred to briefly by the author's last name and an abbreviated title of the article.

3. Make a separate note card for each topic on which you take notes. This card (see Figure 5-3) should contain (1) a brief statement of the topic, (2) the author's last name (use first name or first and middle initials also when two or more authors by the same last name have been consulted), (3) a brief title of the book or article (where needed), (4) a copy of the text material of interest, and (5) the number of the page on which the copied passage appears. If the passage extends over several pages, give the pages on which it begins and ends (thus: pp. 35–54).

   Be careful to enclose material within quotation marks (as in Figure 5-3) when it is a direct copy from the consulted work; otherwise, it may (through forgetfulness) slip into your report as your own work. Your own comments can be readily identified on these cards by the absence of quotation marks.

4. Stack the bibliography cards alphabetically by author's name, and the note cards alphabetically by topic. Use the cards, as required, in preparing the report.

For a more exhaustive treatment of bibliography and note cards, see Robert M. Schmitz, *Preparing the Research Paper*, 4th ed. (New York: Holt, Rinehart and Winston, Inc., 1959, pp. 28–39).

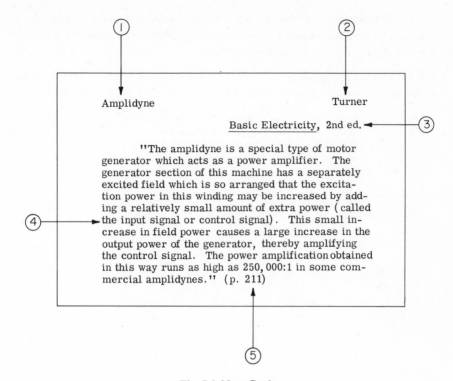

Fig. 5-3 Note Card

EXERCISES

5.1 In a brief coordinated essay, explain which pieces of the data collected in a laboratory experiment you have performed you consider suitable as material for a report. Justify your elimination of the rest.

5.2 List the key persons and the questions you would want to ask them (and the order in which you think they should be asked) if you were to investigate the recent failure of an elevator which your company had installed only two weeks before.

5.3 Explain how a survey might include investigations (Section 5.3), interviews (Section 5.5), and searches of literature (Section 5.6). Develop completely a hypothetical example.

5.4 For a written interview, prepare a questionnaire to determine the percentage of engineers in the interviewee's organization that are engaged in (1) professional work, (2) semiprofessional work, and (3) subprofessional work. The purpose of the interview is to obtain material for a master's thesis. Define *professional*, *semiprofessional*, and *subprofessional* in terms of current standards at your college or plant.

5.5 Conduct a literature search and prepare a complete set of bibliography cards and note cards on any topic of your choice from your own major field.

6

Making an Outline

After the report material has been collected, it must be organized and written up in a well-ordered pattern. To achieve this, the writer must decide which topic should be discussed first, which next, and so on. The plan for this sequence is the *outline*.

An outline is more than a literary road map serving to keep the writer on a logical track; it is a safeguard against repetition and omission and a guide to stratification of the subject matter. Writing moves faster and surer when it follows an outline. Working from an outline imparts to the report a degree of unity and coherence that can be attained otherwise only through slowly cautious composition or extensive rewriting.

Unless there are so few sections in a report (say, four or less) that they can easily be kept in mind, a written outline should be used. And the outline should be prepared as soon as the collected material has been scrutinized for categories and coverage.

6.1 NATURE OF THE OUTLINE

An outline contains the basic structural elements of a composition. It is therefore the skeleton of the report. It shows the relationships between the various topics to be discussed in the report and their relationship to the broad over-all subject. Further, the outline is a practical plan for the writing of the report: By following it, the writer secures good organization of his text and is able to determine the status of the work at any instant. In addition to this, the headings of the outline automatically furnish the elements, in proper sequence, for the table of contents. (See the table of contents of this book.)

Not only does a good outline help the writer to think analytically about his subject, but the logical organization it imparts to the report facilitates the reader's grasp of the subject and of the interrelations within the text. The mechanical structure of the outline shows which topics are of first importance and which of lesser importance, and also which are equal in rank and which are subordinate. This leads the writer to distribute his emphasis in a fashion true to the facts.

6.2 FORMS OF OUTLINES

The outline, as a mechanical structure, may be considered simply an orderly list of words, phrases, or sentences that designate or suggest the nature and sequence of topics to be discussed. The elements in this list are numbered or lettered to show their rank.

Outlines are classified as to *form* according to the way their elements are numbered or lettered. Two forms are widely used: *letter-number* and *decimal*.

In the letter-number form, first-order (principal) items are labeled with capital Roman numerals (I, II, III, . . .), second-order with capital letters (A, B, C, . . .), third-order with Arabic numerals (1, 2, 3, . . .), fourth-order with lower-case letters (a, b, c, . . .), fifth-order with lower-case Roman numerals (i, ii, iii, . . .), and sixth-order with lower-case letters in parentheses: (a), (b), (c), ... A period follows each except the sixth-order letters.

In the so-called decimal form, the first-order (principal) items are labeled with whole numbers (1.0, 2.0, 3.0, . . .), second-order with a number plus one decimal place (1.1, 1.2, 1.3, . . .), third-order with a number plus two "decimal" places (1.1.1, 1.1.2, 1.1.3; 1.2.1, 1.2.2, 1.2.3; 1.3.1, 1.3.2, 1.3.3; . . .), fourth-order with a number plus three "decimal" places (1.1.1.1, 1.1.1.2, 1.1.1.3; 1.1.2.1, 1.1.2.2, 1.1.2.3; . . .). To prevent unwieldiness, subordination is seldom carried beyond the fourth figure. It is obvious that this is not really decimal notation; an extra point or two is used in some cases (as in 1.1.1 to distinguish this label, the first third-order subordinate under 1.1, from 1.11, the eleventh second-order subordinate under 1.0. Some writers use hyphens instead of periods between the numerals (thus: 1-1-1-2).

The letter-number sequence for one principal item (I) and its subdivisions is shown below:

I.
   A.
      1.
         a.
            i.
               (a)
               (b)
             ii.
               (a)
               (b)

      b.
        i.
          (a)
          (b)
        ii.
          (a)
          (b)
    2.
      a.
        i.
          (a)
          (b)
        ii.
          (a)
          (b)
      b.
        i.
          (a)
          (b)
        ii.
          (a)
          (b)

B.
  1.
      a.
        i.
          (a)
          (b)
        ii.
          (a)
          (b)
      b.
        i.
          (a)
          (b)
        ii.
          (a)
          (b)
  2.
      a.
        i.
          (a)
          (b)

              ii.
                    (a)
                    (b)
        b.
            i.
                    (a)
                    (b)
            ii.
                    (a)
                    (b)

The same pattern is repeated under principal items II, III, IV, ... Although only two supporting items are shown in each class (A,B; 1,2; a,b; . . .), the number may be extended as far as necessary. Note that each element is indented according to its class. Note also the coordination and subordination of topics indicated by the uniform system of indentation: A and B are equal to each other but are subordinate to I, the first 1 and 2 are equal to each other but are subordinate to A, the second 1 and 2 are equal to each other but are subordinate to B, the first a and b are equal to each other but are subordinate to 1, the second a and b are equal to each other but are subordinate to 2, and so on. This relationship is sometimes expressed by a set of quasi equations: $I = A + B + \ldots n$, $A = 1 + 2 + \ldots n$, $1 = a + b + \ldots n$, $a = i + ii + \ldots n$, $i = (a) + (b) + \ldots (n)$.

The decimal sequence for two principal items (1.0 and 2.0) and their subdivisions is shown below:

        1.0
          1.1
            1.1.1
              1.1.1.1
              1.1.1.2
            1.1.2
              1.1.2.1
              1.1.2.2
          1.2
            1.2.1
              1.2.1.1
              1.2.1.2
            1.2.2
              1.2.2.1
              1.2.2.2
        2.0
          2.1

2.1.1
    2.1.1.1
    2.1.1.2
2.1.2
    2.1.2.1
    2.1.2.2
2.2
  2.2.1
    2.2.1.1
    2.2.1.2
  2.2.2
    2.2.2.1
    2.2.2.2

Note here also the coordination and subordination of topics indicated by the uniform system of indentation: 1.1 and 1.2 are equal to each other but are subordinate to 1.0, 1.1.1 and 1.1.2 are equal to each other but are subordinate to 1.1 (similarly, 1.2.1 and 1.2.2 are equal to each other but are subordinate to 1.2), 1.1.1.1 and 1.1.1.2 are equal to each other but are subordinate to 1.1.1 (similarly, 1.1.2.1 and 1.1.2.2 are equal to each other but subordinate to 1.1.2), and so on. This relationship is also sometimes expressed by a set of quasi equations: $1.0 = 1.1 + 1.2 + \ldots 1.n$, $1.1 = 1.1.1 + 1.1.2 + \ldots 1.1.n$, $1.1.1 = 1.1.1.1 + 1.1.1.2 + \ldots 1.1.1.n$.

6.3 TYPES OF OUTLINES

After the form of outline has been chosen (Section 6.2), the various topics of the report material are fitted into the framework according to their coordination and subordination.

Outlines are classified by *type* according to the way in which information entered into each compartment of the outline is cast. Three types are widely used: *topical*, *word-phrase*, and *sentence*. In the following illustrations, the same material is outlined in each of these three types. The topical outline names the topics to be discussed but goes no further:

    I. Metals available
      A. Steel
        1. Advantages
        2. Disadvantages
      B. Aluminium
        1. Advantages
        2. Disadvantages

    II. Finishes available

        A. Baked enamel

           1. Advantages

           2. Disadvantages

        B. Air-dried enamel

           1. Advantages

           2. Disadvantages

Entries in the word-phrase outline give a single word or simple phrase, which is sufficient to suggest to the writer what is to be said:

    I. Two metals available

        A. Steel

           1. Strong

           2. Heavy

        B. Aluminum

           1. Lightweight

           2. Soft

    II. Choice of two finishes

        A. Baked enamel

           1. Permanent, chip-proof

           2. Requires oven treatment

        B. Air-dried enamel

           1. Simply applied

           2. Easily defaced

Entries in the sentence outline give information in the form of a sentence (often the topic sentence of a paragraph) and provide the first step of the actual writing:

    I. Two metals may be used in making control boxes.

        A. Steel is the first choice.

           1. It is strong and rugged.

           2. However, it also makes the box heavy and is hard to work.

        B. Aluminum is the second choice.

           1. It is lightweight and easily worked.

           2. However, it is soft and easily dented.

    II. Two paint finishes are available.

        A. Baked enamel is recommended by the sales dept.

           1. This finish is tough and durable.

           2. It is expensive because of the need for oven curing.

B. Air-dried enamel is used on our present boxes.
   1. It is easily sprayed on, and less expensive.
   2. However, it chips if abused.

Some outlines prepared for the writer's exclusive use contain elements of all three types.

The type of outline chosen depends upon individual demands and the writer's preference. The topical type is adequate when the report is merely being mapped out (the report parts list given in Section 2.1B is such an outline). The word-phrase type is useful when the writer needs a hint but not an entire sentence. The sentence type is necessary when the writer wants to record an entire statement that can later be expanded into a paragraph.

6.4 ASSEMBLING THE OUTLINE

It is a good habit to make an outline for any piece of writing. After some experience, this becomes automatic. Like any other composition, however, an outline may be the result of a first draft and several revisions, which means that it should be corrected and altered as required. Although a writer should strive to put his outline into final form before he writes from it, entering all pertinent items in their logical places, he must be ready to alter the outline as his writing progresses if he discovers omissions, excesses, or the need for rearrangement.

Follow this procedure when putting an outline together:

1. Read the pieces of collected material carefully.

2. Decide the best sequence for presenting the material in a report. (Sometimes this sequence is dictated, as in the formal-report parts list in Section 2.1B).

3. Select the form of outline (see Section 6.2).

4. Select the type of outline (see Section 6.3).

5. Make the outline by fitting items of material into the numbered or lettered compartments in accordance with the type (Section 6.3).

6. Carefully inspect the completed outline and revise it if necessary.

In addition to an outline for the entire report, one is often needed for the writing of a section in the report (for example, abstract, introduction, discussion).

EXERCISES

6.1 Prepare a letter-number, topical outline of the specimen student report in Appendix 2.

6.2 Prepare a decimal, word-phrase outline of the specimen professional report in Appendix 4.

6.3 Explain in a 500-word article the merits and demerits that, in your opinion, seem evident in (*a*) the two forms and (*b*) three types of outlines described in this chapter.

6.4 Discuss fully any advantages which you think might accrue from the use of a combination outline (that is, one containing a mixture of topical, word-phrase, and sentence elements).

6.5 Make a library search of material on engineers in management, and prepare an outline for a report based upon your findings.

7

Writing a Rough Draft

With the report material collected and sorted and the outline completed, the actual writing can get under way. This initial writing step will produce the first version of the report as a piece of connected prose derived from the mass of notes and other material collected earlier. Naturally, it will be imperfect — that is why it is called a *rough* draft — but it will be refined during several revisions. Almost never is a first draft of such high quality, technically or rhetorically, that it can serve as the final version of a composition.

It might seem that rough drafting is so obvious a task that nothing need be said about it. But this is far from true — a report can bog down in this first writing stage for want of procedural skill on the part of the writer. Rough drafting can be a stumbling block to the uninitiated.

There is no talisman that will ensure success in writing a rough draft, but there are a few sensible rules which, if followed by the report writer, will provide good direction for writing. These rules are the substance of the present chapter.

7.1 NATURE OF THE ROUGH DRAFT

The rough draft is the first, trial version of the written report. Although the writer tries to make it as good as he can without slowing his writing or thinking, the rough draft contains errors and faults that will be corrected in later drafts. The rough draft is thus the report in its most primitive and unpolished form.

Nobody expects a rough draft to be a work of art. Admittedly, there are good ones and bad ones and a writer's ability to turn out good ones (that is, rough drafts that are easy to revise) will improve with experience. But no new writer should be alarmed at, or discouraged by, the crudeness of his first drafts, nor should he squander his time on dressing them up at this point in the writing of the report.

7.2   GENERAL WRITING PROCEDURE

No facetiousness is intended by the epigram "the best way to write a rough draft is to sit down and write it." The literal truth is that getting something down on paper is a hurdle that stops many a new writer dead. Therefore, the correct move is to start writing at once — you have reviewed the collected material and prepared an outline; now there is nothing to wait for.

The first advice is to start writing immediately. The second is to write *fast*, putting your thoughts on paper before you forget them. This means that you should not stop to make corrections or to beautify sentences (save that for the revisions) but should record the ideas as they come, giving no thought at this time to correct spelling, grammar, sentence structure, and paragraphing. Once the material is on paper, it may be corrected. The important matter at this point is to get it down, however imperfectly; the faster you write, the less chance there will be for dawdling.

Observing the following points will be helpful when you write a rough draft:

1. Know the subject matter. You will have read, checked, and sorted the report material before making an outline. Now clear up any points you do not understand.

2. Follow the outline. The common method is to progress through the outline from beginning to end, finishing the writing in each category before moving to the next. In some instances, however, a nonsequential attack may be favored (see Section 7.3). Rough draft the entire report before revising, unless you are responsible for only one section. Do not rough a part and then attempt to revise it fully before moving on to the next.

3. Use your favorite method of first drafting (longhand, typewriter, dictating machine), but remember that the rough draft must finally be on paper for reading and correcting, so transcribe it as soon as practicable if you dictate it to a machine or write it out in longhand.

4. Double-space all sentences so that corrections and additions may be written between the lines.

5. Handle the rough draft to suit your own convenience: Make corrections, cross-outs, erasures, insertions, and notes to yourself with no concern for attractiveness or cleanness. Use private abbreviations or your own shorthand freely. The sole criterion is *your* ability to read the draft. The rough draft is for your own use; if it is to circulate, type a cleaned-up version incorporating your corrections and changes.

6. Refer freely to illustrations and supplementary matter. You will already have selected some illustrations and planned others during the

preliminary planning stage. You will also have selected or planned supplementary material, such as charts and tables. Assign numbers (Figure 1, Chart A, Table 5), even if temporarily, and refer to this material by the numbers as you write the rough draft (for example, "Component reliability figures are given in Table B.").

7. If you have a list of references, complete it and keep it nearby so that you can refer to its entries while writing the rough draft. See reference citations on pages 1, 5, and 11 of the specimen student report in Appendix 2, and see Section 2.1C (part 18) for instructions in using the list of references.

8. Number the pages of the draft consecutively.

9. Check the completed rough draft against the outline and collected material to determine what has been omitted and what has been inadequately discussed. If possible, allow the rough draft to "cool off" for a day or two before you check it; this will increase your objective detachment when you read it.

7.3 WRITING SEQUENCE

It has already been stated that the writer usually follows the outline closely when preparing a rough draft, developing the various parts of the report in the sequence in which they are established in the outline. However, the sequence may be ignored when the occasion demands if this can be done logically. For example, an appendix might be put together ahead of the rest of the report because necessary collaborators happen to be available only at the time, and a bibliography might be completed first because it will be cited in the rest of the writing.

Often, the parts of a technical report must be written in a chronological order that differs from the sequence of these parts in the report. The formal report, for instance, contains the following parts in the order given: preface, acknowledgments, abstract or summary, introduction, discussion, conclusions, recommendations, bibliography or list of references. However, these parts are rough drafted in the following order:

> Bibliography
> Discussion
> List of references (see below)
> Conclusions
> Recommendations
> Introduction
> Abstract or summary
> Preface

The reason for this difference is logical: Data must first be presented in the discussion before there is anything about which to draw conclusions or make recommendations. Similarly, the discussion, conclusions, and recommendations must be completed before the writer can be sure what information will be pertinent in the introduction; the entire draft must be completed before the abstract or summary of it can be written; and all of the sections must be completed before the preface can reasonably be written. The bibliography is completed first, since it will be referred to in the rough draft (see Section 7.2). The numbered list of references must be compiled while the discussion is being written.

The elements shown above are not the only ones in a formal report of course (see Section 2.1B), but they are the ones normally handled in the first rough draft. Other elements are introduced in later revisions and in the final preparation: title, cover, title page, letter of transmittal, approvals, distribution list, acknowledgments, table of contents, list of illustrations, appendixes, glossary, and index.

7.4   ILLUSTRATIVE EXAMPLE

The following passage is the rough draft of the introduction section of the specimen student report in Appendix 2. Compare this draft with the introduction itself, on pages 1 and 2 of the report, to see how the student corrected and rearranged the material, through revisions, for final presentation in the report.

I.   *Introduction*

Varistors are 2-terminal devices. There are many kinds of them. A common name is "voltage-variable resistor" — but current is mostly used to vary them. The silicon carbide resistor is one, so is the incandescent lamp filament and the thermistor (which is also temperature sensitive). All varistors are non-ohmic, that is they don't follow Ohm's law (E/I isn't constant). The resistance of the varistor changes with current or voltage. We thought a germanium diode (or any other semiconductor diode for that matter) might make a fairly good cheap and dirty varistor especially if it was biased in the forward direction (with anode connected to positive, cathode negative). A previous experiment gave this idea.

The forward curve of a diode (semiconductor type) is nonlinear like that of a commercial varistor (Refer to references 1 and 2). All diodes — copper oxide, selenium, gallium arsenide, silicon — act this way. But 1N34A germanium diodes are cheap and plentiful. We could get 100 of them for testing.

Our expectations were borne out — the diode does give good varistor action. The tests are described in this report. Also offered are test data, advantages and disadvantages, resistance properties of the 1N34A, and recommendations for more work along this line.

There are many applications for varistors, where dc must be applied to them and also where a variable dc is already present in a circuit.

It is apparent that the writer got his ideas on paper as fast as he could, without worrying about mechanics. Later, he had plenty of time during the revision phases to correct the English, move sentences around, and eliminate repetition.

EXERCISES

7.1 Using the outline you made in Exercise 6.5, write a rough draft of the report on engineers in management.

7.2 Author Ernest Hemingway felt that the finished appearance of typewritten copy tended to discourage revision, since the typewriter "solidifies one's sentences before they are ready to print." Other writers have no objection to typing a rough draft, and even to making corrections with the machine. Write an essay of approximately 1000 words explaining the advantages and disadvantages, as you see them, of typewritten and handwritten rough drafts.

7.3 Describe the writing sequence for a rough draft of an informal report. (See Section 2.2B for parts of an informal report.)

7.4 Explain why rough drafting may be required in the preparation of such auxiliary parts of a report as title, cover, title page, letter of transmittal, approvals, distribution list, acknowledgments, table of contents, list of illustrations, glossary, bibliography, and index.

7.5 Using the sentence-type outline in Section 6.3, rough draft a discussion of control boxes. Look up any additional information you may need on making and painting small metal boxes.

8

Selecting and Preparing Illustrations

Some reports need many illustrations, others none at all. Most reports fall somewhere between these extremes. Illustrations (collectively called *artwork*) are graphic aids and should be used in technical reports for their ability to clarify a description and to show concrete details which otherwise would require many words to describe adequately. They should never be used solely to dress up a report. Illustrations of some types are, of course, indispensable to an explanation: block diagrams, circuit diagrams, flow diagrams, piping diagrams, and organization charts.

The subject of illustration is introduced at this point because by the time the rough draft is started, the writer must have decided on the illustrations in order to write about them. Naturally, additional illustrations will suggest themselves as the writing progresses through its various phases, but the nucleus of artwork should be chosen in the preliminary planning phase.

As mentioned in Section 4.5, some of the illustrations selected in preliminary planning will be already finished artwork, and the others will be assigned for preparation to illustrators and photographers so that they will be ready when needed for insertion into the report. The writer can keep finished artwork, or copies of it, before him as he works; and he can keep rough sketches of the artwork that is in preparation.

The basic illustrative material discussed in the present chapter will be sufficient for a great many reports. Integration of artwork into the report is discussed in Chapters 9 and 10.

8.1   TYPES OF ILLUSTRATIONS

The illustrative material used in technical reports may be classified as (1) halftones, (2) line drawings, (3) combination line and halftone art, (4) graphs, (5) charts, and (6) tables. These illustrations are usually all black and white, although color is used occasionally. Each classification is described separately in Sections 8.3 to 8.8.

76

8.2   METHODS OF REPRODUCTION

Illustrations are incorporated into reports either directly or by reproduction. Direct binding of an original illustration into a report is usually limited to one-report editions, although photographs are sometimes put into multiple-run reports in this manner.

How an illustration is to be reproduced depends upon how the report itself will be reproduced. If the report is letterpress printed, for example, cuts must be made of all illustrations (copper engravings for the halftone pictures and zinc etchings for the line drawings, as a rule). The illustrations must have been prepared to meet engraving requirements. If Multilith offset reproduction is used, the illustrations must be made on the masters used for printing the report. For stencil-type reproduction, such as mimeograph, they must be made on the stencils. For xerographic reproduction, the illustrations should be integral with the final copy, that is, drawn on, or patched onto, the report pages. For photo-offset reproduction, the illustrations are usually handled separately, and incorporated by the printer in the plate-making process.

All of the processes except letterpress maintain a 1:1 relationship between size of the original and size of the reproduction. Illustrations intended for letterpress or photo-offset, however, may be prepared up to twice the intended size of the reproduction, with lines thickened in the same ratio in line drawings. This permits better treatment of detail during the preparation of the art.

8.3   HALFTONE PICTURES

Halftones provide a wide range of light and shade that aims to show the subject, in three-dimensional representation, as it appears to the eye. They include photographs, airbrush renderings, and wash drawings.

A. Photographs. For clear reproduction, a photograph must be sharp and contrasty, even harsh to the eye, and it must be free of shadows and glare effects. It should be large, so that it can be retouched easily if this is required (8 in. × 10 in. glossy contact prints are excellent for the engraver). A photograph is required whenever a bona fide image is demanded. Figure 8-1 shows a typical technical photograph (of a standard cell of the same kind shown in the line drawing, Figure 8-2).

One step in the engraving process comprises photographing the photograph itself onto a sensitized plate through a screen (this is what imparts the familiar dot pattern to printed pictures) and this, together with the printing process, tends to soften the picture. If the original photograph is already soft, the picture will be fuzzy in the final printing; hence, the need for an ex-

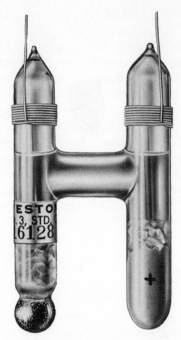

Fig. 8-1   Typical Retouched Photograph (Weston Standard Cell).

tremely sharp picture to start with. The technical photographer works for a sharp texture, unlike most portrait photographers, who try, instead, for a soft, glamorous picture.

B. Airbrush Rendering. This type of illustration has all of the realism of the photograph, which it resembles. But since it is manually executed, it can be conceived from the imagination — that is, it can show an object that does not yet exist. Since the artist is able to work from blueprints, airbrush renderings are thus frequently used when it is necessary to show what a finished device will look like.

An airbrush rendering can show many things that a photograph ordinarily cannot, such as an x-ray view of an engine or a cutaway view of a missile.

Because the ink or paint is applied to the paper by air spraying, rather than by brushing, airbrush work has a smoothness of tone that simulates photography.

The reproduction requirements for an airbrush rendering are identical with those for the photograph. That is, the rendering should be sharp and contrasty and, if a halftone cut is to be made from it, it should be twice the intended size of the reproduction.

C. Wash Drawing. The wash drawing is approximately similar to an airbrush rendering in appearance and has similar pictorial advantages.

Instead of air pressure, a hair-type brush is used to apply the ink or paint in the same way that a water color is painted.

The reproduction requirements for the wash drawing are identical with those for the photograph and airbrush rendering.

8.4 LINE DRAWINGS

Line drawings are the commonest type of illustration used in technical reports. The specimen reports in Appendixes 2 and 4 contain drawings of this type (Figure 1 in Appendix 2; and Figures 1, 8, and 16 in Appendix 4).

Line drawings, as the name indicates, are composed mainly of lines, but may also have shaded, crosshatched, or solid areas but not the gradation of light and shade afforded by halftone pictures. They are executed in black India ink, and for letterpress reproduction should be twice the intended size of the reproduction (with the lines twice as thick as they are to appear in reproduction). For reproduction by blueprint, mimeograph, Multilith, or Xerox, a line drawing may be the same size as the intended reproduction.

Line drawings include (1) views of objects, (2) circuit diagrams, (3) block diagrams, (4) flow diagrams, (5) maps and plans, and (6) piping diagrams. Each of these drawings may be easily labeled for identification of parts.

A. Views. A view is a line drawing that attempts to show an object as it appears to the eye. But it is not always three-dimensional: A front view, side view, or end view of an object is flat, and so is a conventional cross-sectional view. Three-dimensional views include isometric, oblique, perspective, and exploded types. All of these are familiar to engineers, technicians, and draftsmen.

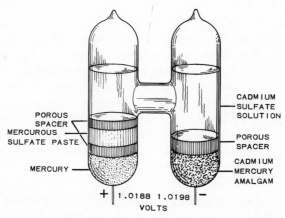

Fig. 8-2 View-type Line Drawing (Weston Standard Cell).

Figure 8-2 shows a view of a standard cell similar to the one shown in photograph in Figure 8-1. Note the three-dimensional effect and the clear identification of the parts.

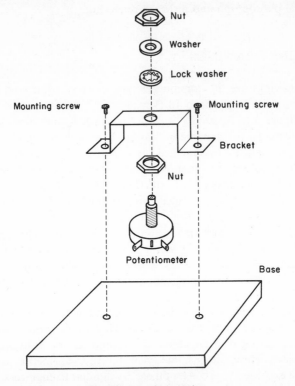

Fig. 8-3 Exploded View.

Figure 8-3 shows a typical exploded view. The subject here is a small potentiometer mounted on a metal bracket which is fastened to a base plate. See also Figure 16 in the specimen professional report in Appendix 4, for an exploded view of the Saturn IVB-stage rocket. An exploded view shows how the parts of an assembly fit together, by depicting them as if the assembly had blown apart but with all parts correctly aligned. This clarifies details that would be hidden in a view of the intact assembly. For an exploded-view photograph, the assembly must actually be dismantled and the parts carefully positioned before the camera to give the effect, which is more easily produced by a drawing such as Figure 8-3.

The purpose of cross-sectional and cutaway views is to show the interior and exterior of an assembly simultaneously. The cross section (Figure 8-4) does this two-dimensionally, and the cutaway (Figure 8-5) three-dimensionally. When used to depict a complicated device, the cutaway view requires less

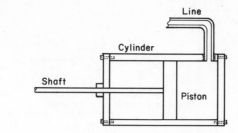

Fig. 8-4 Cross-sectional View.

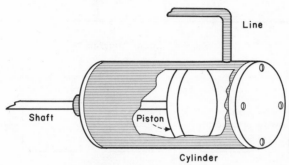

Fig. 8-5 Cutaway View.

visualizing effort on the part of the viewer than does the cross section, since it shows the cut-open device as it would appear to the eye. Actual cutaways have been made by sawing through a device and then photographing, but this is destructive and sometimes impossible. When the photographic effect is desired, a halftone cutaway can be made by airbrush rendering or wash drawing.

B. Circuit Diagrams. A circuit diagram may be regarded as employing a kind of pictorial shorthand for showing components and how they are wired together in electrical or electronic circuits. Standard symbols represent the components, and the lines running between them represent the wires connecting them. This diagram therefore is a highly simplified picture (or schematic) of the wired equipment. Figure 8-6 is the circuit diagram of a transistorized electronic voltmeter. Here, the symbols marked R are resistors, S switches, Q transistors, B a battery, C a capacitor, and M a milliammeter.

C. Block Diagrams. A circuit diagram for a system containing a number of stages, each in turn containing many components and a great deal of wiring, can be very complicated and hard to follow. For use in conjunction with explanations of behavior, the diagram can be simplified by substituting a square or rectangle for each of the stages and connecting these *blocks* together by a single line to show the normal flow of information or material through the system.

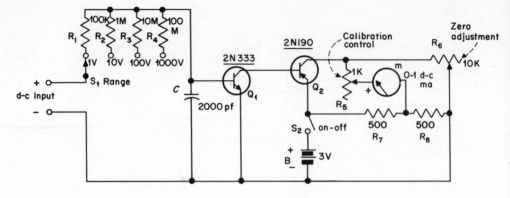

Fig. 8-6   Circuit Diagram.

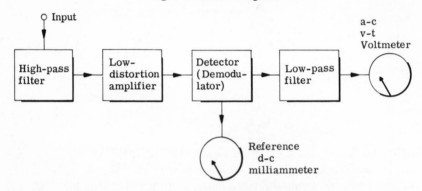

Fig. 8-7   Block Diagram.

Figure 8-7 is such a block diagram of an intermodulation meter. The function of each stage in the instrument is shown by the title of the corresponding block. The arrowheads on the connecting lines show that the test signal moves through the circuit from the input terminal to the two meters. This signal is modified successively by the stages through which it passes.

D. Flow Diagrams. A flow diagram is somewhat similar to a block diagram. In the former, the blocks usually represent stages or steps in a process.

Figure 8-8 is a flow diagram identifying, and showing the order of, steps in the photographic process, from the act of exposure (taking of the picture) to the delivery of a finished print. Similar diagrams are constructed for the flow of materials through any processing or manufacturing sequence, information through a digital computer, and any other sequence in which successive operations are performed on some medium.

E. Maps and Plans. Maps and plans are common enough to need no elaboration here. Maps found in technical reports include the following

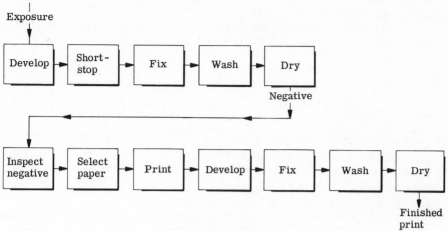

Fig. 8-8 Flow Diagram.

types: geographical, property-boundary, coastline, topographical, and geological. Plans include those of buildings, subdivisions of a building, machine installations, wiring, piping, and department layouts.

F. Piping Diagrams. What the circuit diagram is to electrical and electronic systems, the piping diagram is to hydraulic and pneumatic systems. Various symbols in this diagram represent the components (valves, pumps,

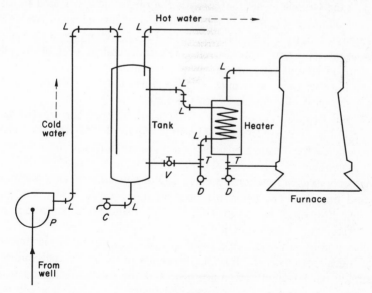

Fig. 8-9 Piping Diagram.

gauges, tanks, and so on) and the lines drawn between them represent the pipes connecting the components.

Figure 8-9 is a simple piping diagram for a hot-water supply using well water. The symbols marked C are cocks, D drains, L elbows, P pumps, T tees, and V valves.

8.5   COMBINATION LINE AND HALFTONE ART

Combination art consists of some combination of photograph, airbrush rendering, wash drawing, and line drawing. An example is a piping diagram in which the valves and other components are photographs rather than drawn symbols. Combination drawings are often used in technical instruction manuals and reports intended for semiprofessional personnel.

8.6   GRAPHS

A graph is a pictorial representation of the variation of one quantity with respect to another, or a pictorial comparison of two or more quantities. It displays at a glance information that could be obtained otherwise only by pondering and comparing a mass of numerical data. Familiar kinds of graphs are the *line* type, *vertical bar* type, and *horizontal bar* type.

A. Line Graphs. The line graph is the one most often used to display technical data (see Figure 2 in the specimen student report in Appendix 2; and Figures 2, 5, 6, 7, 9, 10, 11, 12, 13, 14, 15, 17, 18, and 19 in the specimen professional report in Appendix 4). The independent variable is plotted along the horizontal axis, and the dependent variable along the vertical axis. One or both of these axes may be either linear or logarithmic, whichever permits the most efficient display of the data.

B. Bar Graphs. Less familiar to the laboratory worker are vertical and horizontal bar graphs. These are shown in Figure 8-10(*a*) and (*b*). The two graphs offered for illustration show how a certain company uses the services of its fifty engineers. The vertical bar graph (Figure 8-10*a*) shows the number of engineers in each function: research and design, field service, manufacturing, and miscellaneous (standards, production control, inspection, and so on). The horizontal bar graph (Figure 8-10*b*) shows the percentage of the engineering staff in each function.

Bar graphs are invaluable for displaying data both for technical and nontechnical readers. The bar length reveals immediately the comparative magnitude of the quantities concerned, and the exact magnitude is easily determined by referring to the numbered scale. This type of graph is used extensively in an effort to simplify and vivify the presentation of dull nu-

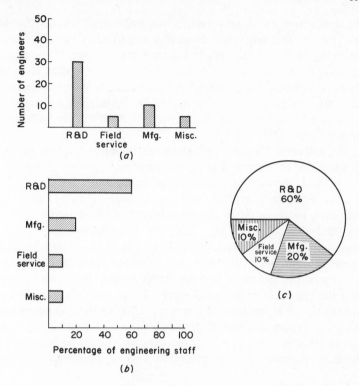

Fig. 8-10 Three Ways of Displaying the Same Data on Using Engineering Personnel. (*a*) Vertical bar graph. (*b*) Horizontal bar graph. (*c*) Pie chart.

merical data in reports to be read by laymen and nontechnical executives. An example of this is replacement of the bars with tall, medium, and short men, buildings, trees, machines, stacks of coins, and so on — each drawn to the proper scale.

8.7 CHARTS

A chart, like a graph, is a pictorial presentation of information generally concerning compared factors. Common types are the *pie* (or *circular*) chart and the *organization* chart. Some authorities call the bar graphs (Section 8.6B) and flow diagrams (Section 8.4D) charts also.

A. Pie Charts. Figure 8-10(*c*) shows a typical pie chart. The origin of the name is obvious from the resemblance of the figure to the well-known pastry. A less colloquial term, often used, is *circle chart*.

The pie chart in Figure 8-10(*c*), like the bar graphs in Figure 8-10(*a*) and (*b*), shows how a company uses its fifty engineers. Each of the slices of the pie is proportional to the percentage of engineers in the indicated functions, corresponding to the percentages in Figure 8-10(*b*). Thus, 60 percent of the engineers are in research and design, so the large slice labeled R & D is 60 percent of the circle. The pie chart is invaluable for giving a quick, easily grasped picture of proportions, but it may not be interpreted quantitatively as readily as a bar graph. For that reason, its segments are usually labeled numerically as in Figure 8-10(*c*).

B. Organization Charts. This chart, as its name implies, generally is used to show line of command in an organization.

Figure 8-11 shows a specimen organization chart for an engineering department. For simplicity, this chart has not been extended below the professional level, but it could be carried further to include technicians, model builders, and clerical personnel. The line of command moves vertically from top to bottom of the chart; posts of equal rank are aligned horizontally. Thus, each of the engineers (lower-most row) are of equal rank, but report to different heads: the systems engineers report to the chief systems engineer, the electrical engineers to the chief electrical engineer, and the mechanical engineers to the chief mechanical engineer. Each of these chiefs is equal in rank and they report to the executive engineer. The latter is assisted by a technical consultant who has no jurisdiction over any of the personnel under the executive engineer, and therefore is aligned horizontally with him.

8.8 TABLES

A table presents data in rows and columns for identification and interpretation. For typical tables, see pages 1 and 2 of the specimen memorandum report (Appendix 1), page 2 of the specimen student report (Appendix 2), pages 6 and 25–29 of the specimen professional report (Appendix 4), and page 2 of the specimen laboratory test report (Appendix 5).

A table should be placed as close as possible to the place at which it is first mentioned in the text. However, if tables are so long or numerous as to impede reading, they should be placed in an appendix.

8.9 IDENTIFYING ILLUSTRATIONS

An illustration is identified by means of a number (assigned consecutively) and a brief descriptive title called a *caption* or *legend* which is generally, but not invariably, written on the same line as the number. Drawings, half-

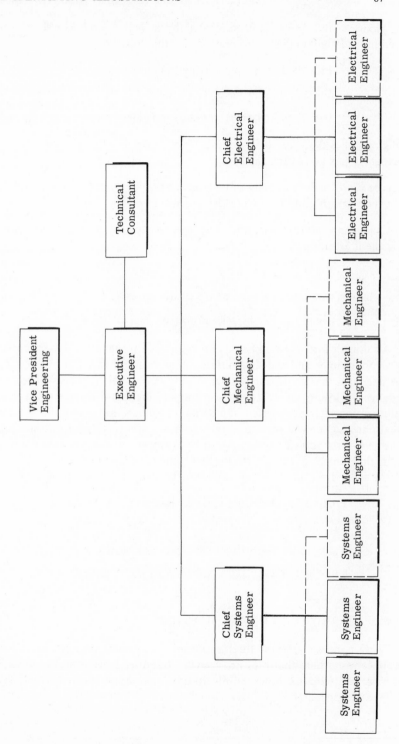

Fig. 8-11 Organization Chart.

tone pictures, and graphs are designated by a figure number and caption placed immediately under, or to one side of, the illustration:

FIGURE 1. Oil Trap for the Vacuum System

Fig. 23. Liquid Level Transmitter

FIG. 7. VERTICAL TURBINE-TYPE PUMP

Sometimes it is desirable to give, instead of a simple title, a descriptive or explanatory passage in the caption:

Figure 13. The development of underground voids by drainage is shown above in (*a*), (*b*), and (*c*). Note the mushroom action.

Charts and tables are identified by similar captions placed immediately *above* the illustration:

Table 2. Suspended-Roof Sag Data

TABLE VI. ANNUAL STATE HIGHWAY COSTS

Chart 10. Earthquake Forces on Tall Buildings

All illustrations are numbered consecutively throughout a report unless the report is long and the illustrations numerous. In the latter case, it is safer to restart the numbering with each chapter or section. This will reduce the danger of losing count. It will also simplify the job of correcting, should an illustration later be inserted in a series — only the following illustrations in that one chapter will then need renumbering; otherwise, every illustration to the end of the report would have to be changed. In the repeated number system, the number has two parts, the first being the chapter or section number and the second the illustration number. The two are joined by a hyphen:

FIGURE 5-8. Residual Gas Analyzer

FIG. XV-3. HIGH-INTENSITY MONOCHROMATOR

Table 10-9. Viscosity of Common Lubricants

Chart 6-1. Organization of the Research Division

8.10 PLACING ILLUSTRATIONS

There is no set rule for the location of illustrations in a report. They can appear anywhere that they are needed. Because of the topics dealt with in the various sections, however, illustrations appear most often in the discussion and appendix.

The occasional practice of placing *all* illustrations in the appendix is to be discouraged, since this compels the reader to travel back and forth between the body and back of the report, which is distracting. But some illustrations, such as supplementary maps and drawings and large folded diagrams and charts, normally are placed in the appendix or in a separate volume.

8.11   REFERRING TO ILLUSTRATIONS

Each illustration must be cited at least once. Do not insert an illustration and then ignore it in the text, leaving the determination of its significance to the reader. Make the citation definite: "Figure 16 shows . . . ," "See Table 4-7," and so on.

EXERCISES

8.1 Prepare a table, with a suitable caption, showing data obtained in a recent laboratory exercise in your major field. (These data should show action of at least one independent variable and one dependent variable.)

8.2 Using the data from Exercise 8.1, prepare a line graph, properly captioned.

8.3 Prepare a vertical bar graph based upon the following information: Company X has 64 employees. Of these, 15 are in professional work, 31 clerical, 13 service and support, and 5 maintenance. Show the percentage in each category. Supply a caption.

8.4 Prepare a horizontal bar graph based upon the following information: Five groups of flashers were placed on a life test. Group 1 ran 3000 hours to failure; Group 2, 5800 hours; Group 3, 7604 hours; Group 4, 10,000 hours; and Group 5, 10,050 hours. Supply a caption.

8.5 Draw a pie chart comparing the time spent during a semester — in your major field — in lecture attendance, laboratory work, field work, and homework. Prepare a caption.

8.6 Make a list of illustrations that might possibly be used for Chapter 1 of this book. Either make rough sketches or write a brief description of each illustration. Write a caption for each illustration.

8.7 Would you use a block diagram or flow diagram to illustrate the sequence of steps in the operation of a gasoline engine? Explain fully, citing the advantages and disadvantages of your chosen method.

8.8 Discuss the advantages and disadvantages of using combination line and halftone art (specifically, a mixture of photographs and line drawings) to illustrate a set of instructions for setting up a signal generator, impedance bridge, and oscilloscope in a test setup for measuring resistance, inductance, and capacitance.

8.9 Describe fully the illustrations you would consider appropriate in an annual report to the stockholders of a small engineering corporation. The stockholders cover a broad occupational cross section.

8.10 Technical report editors avoid front-cover illustrations unless the latter are decided by graphic arts professionals in consultation with company officials, and are tastefully executed. Describe a possible front-cover illustration for the specimen professional report in Appendix 4. If you consider such an illustration inappropriate for this report, explain your reasons.

9

Revising and Rewriting

This is the improvement phase. Correcting the mistakes in the rough draft, adding items which were forgotten or have lately been suggested, removing items which have proved irrelevant or superfluous, polishing the mechanics — all of these are the activities of revising and rewriting. Unfortunately, no amount of writing experience seems able to guarantee a perfect first draft, so revision is accepted as a natural procedure even by experienced professionals.

During this phase, the report writer is concerned with all of the details he temporarily ignored, for the sake of speed, when writing the rough draft: language mechanics, logic, style, technical accuracy, and so on. He tries to view the rough draft dispassionately, as if he were correcting somebody else's writing faults. The results will be good if he can be sternly self-critical and will revise with no qualms.

Every writer and editor eventually works out his own best procedure for revising — one which affords maximum accuracy, completeness, and speed and which can be pursued more or less routinely. The best that the present chapter can offer is a core procedure, which an individual writer may expand or modify to suit his particular needs.

9.1 CORRECTION PROCEDURE

As you read the rough draft, be alert for errors and bad writing of all kinds, but avoid looking for too much at one time or you will accomplish less than you should. It is better to make three separate readings, concentrating each time on one correction area, as explained in the following paragraphs.

Read the entire rough draft the first time for technical accuracy and avoid worrying about other matters. Are the statements true? Is the technical content clearly presented or is it puzzling? Are there errors in engineering or mathematics? Are there contradictions? Is there enough illustrative material?

Read the second time for logic. Do the topics follow each other in a meaningful sequence? Are statements and claims adequately supported? Are the conclusions valid? Do the recommendations make sense? Do faults in the outline show up at this point? Is the report carefully structured according to the pattern given in Section 2.1C or one like it?

Read the third time for language mechanics. Be critical of every sentence. Check grammar, spelling, punctuation, sentence structure, sentence variety, and paragraphing. Does the draft lack unity and coherence? (See Section 1.8.) Is the style appropriate to the reporting situation and audience? (See Sections 1.4, 1.7, and 1.8.)

During each of these readings, make your corrections, additions, and deletions on the rough draft itself — unless they are voluminous, in which case you may make them on separate sheets. Number such sheets and refer to them by notes at the point of correction in the draft (for example, "See inserted page 2A"). After you have made all corrections in each of the three readings, carefully read the draft once again for technical accuracy, since corrections of grammar and style sometimes change the technical sense of a statement. Have a qualified second party check your work, if possible.

After you have made all of the corrections and changes on the rough draft and/or on separate pages, type a fresh version — the *second draft* — incorporating all of the revisions. Then read and revise the second draft in the same way that you did the rough draft; and for this, type a *third draft*. Make as many additional revisions and new drafts as necessary until you finally obtain a satisfactorily polished draft.

The principal editorial details you should be concerned with in your revisions are discussed in Sections 9.2 to 9.10 below. Use these sections as a checklist in the critical examination of your rough and revised drafts.

The revision and rewriting phase is slower than the rough drafting phase, because it demands close reading, careful modifying, and more painstaking composition than is needed in roughing.

9.2   GRAMMAR

Careless grammar disparages not only the writer, but his organization and the report. Allow no grammatical error to go uncorrected on the assumption that the reader is not a grammarian — he always seems to know more grammar than was expected. For guidance, see Turner, *Grammar Review for Technical Writers* (New York: Holt, Rinehart and Winston, 1964).[1]

Grammatical errors commonly found in technical compositions include the following ones, shown here with the page in *Grammar Review* on which they are discussed: improper use of trade name (12), wrong form of compound

[1]This book will be referred to hereafter simply as *Grammar Review*.

noun (13), wrong number of noun (14), wrong case of noun (15), incorrect plural of collective noun (16), vague pronoun reference (23), faulty pronoun agreement (32), improper comparison of adjectives and adverbs (41, 60), improper use of auxiliary verb (47), wrong number of verb (48), wrong tense of verb (49, 50, 51), confusing position of adverb (59), confusion of adjective and adverb (43, 60), wrong preposition (69), careless use of restrictive and nonrestrictive elements (19, 78, 84), dangling structures (78, 84), false coining of adjectives (36).

9.3 SPELLING

Bad spelling is a blemish on any piece of writing; it is inexcusable in a technical report. Whether we concur or not, enough people of consequence equate poor spelling with illiteracy and carelessness that we cannot risk this flaw in our reports. It is only natural to assume that men who have carelessly written a report, not caring enough to check spelling, have been careless also in the technical work they are reporting.

Be on the lookout not only for words you have misspelled, but also for typographical errors — the reader has no way of knowing that you accidentally struck the wrong key of the typewriter; he thinks you are a dunce. Let the dictionary be your authority on correct spelling. Also consult the official glossary or stylebook of your technical profession; if the dictionary and the professional glossary disagree on the spelling of a *technical* word, use the spelling given by the glossary.

When the dictionary gives more than one spelling for a word (for example acknowledgment/acknowledgement, gauge/gage, sulfur/sulphur), use the first, or preferred, one.

9.4 PUNCTUATION

A good part of language revision in the rough draft consists of correcting punctuation. This is understandable, because in the hurried writing of the rough draft, punctuation suffers unless the writer is an expert who punctuates automatically.

Full, close punctuation may be tedious but it reduces the chance of misreading and promotes communication of ideas. Use a punctuation mark in each place where it is required (see *Grammar Review*, pages 95–108), as often as necessary. A particularly troublesome punctuation problem is that of hyphenation. This results from our large store of compound technical words and the diverse rules, laid down by company stylebooks, for hyphenating them. Unless you are following a prescribed stylebook which dictates otherwise, use the hyphen fully. In particular, use it to distinguish a compound adjective from a noun modified by an adjective. (Thus: "The chamber operates at *high pressure*," but "This is a *high-pressure* chamber.") For rules of hyphenation, see *Grammar Review*, pages 13, 37, 57, 102, and 103.

When reading a draft, be on the lookout for common errors such as these (the numbers are the pages in *Grammar Review* that may be consulted): omission of punctuation, comma splice (101), misuse of dash (101), unwise use of exclamation point (71, 72), comma omitted from nonrestrictive element (19, 78, 84), dropping of last serial comma (99), apostrophe in inanimate possessive (16).

9.5 SENTENCE VARIETY

The hurried writing of the rough draft has probably yielded a melange of short, choppy sentences and long, rambling ones. Some of the revision will consist of rewriting these sentences. When you rewrite them, observe two rules: (1) fit the sentence to the thought, and (2) vary the sentence pattern to prevent monotony.

Fitting sentence to thought means simply using a compound sentence to express related ideas of equal rank, a complex sentence when one thought is subordinate to another (making sure that you put the independent idea in the main clause, and the dependent idea in the dependent, or subordinate, clause), a compound-complex sentence for a combination of independent and dependent ideas (taking care to express these ideas in the corresponding clauses), and simple sentences for brief, usually independent, simple ideas that ordinarily are not closely related (see *Grammar Review*, pages 91–93).

Varying the sentence pattern means shifting the arrangement of internal elements (words, phrases, clauses) to keep the sentences from all sounding alike. The rough draft is apt to contain mostly short declarative sentences of the basic *subject* + *verb* + *object* pattern; and although the writing might be ever so factual, it is deadly monotonous. A certain variety is achieved by matching sentences and ideas, as explained in the preceding paragraph. Still more may be obtained, where appropriateness and the nature of the idea permit, by varying internal elements. For example, the principal/subordinate relationship of ideas is not disturbed by varying the position of clauses in the following sentences:

The pressure is low because more lawns are being watered at this hour.

Because more lawns are being watered at this hour, the pressure is low.

More lawns are being watered at this hour; therefore, the pressure is low.

This means simply that if you start one sentence with a dependent clause, try starting the next one with an independent clause if this can be done without improperly shading the meaning, and then perhaps use a simple sentence in the next position, and so on. You have at least five patterns to work with (see *Grammar Review*, pages 88–90) and you should use as many of them as are compatible with the text material. Use them as randomly as possible; otherwise, you will introduce a new source of monotony — your pattern of variation.

9.6   SENTENCE QUALITY

Examine your sentences ruthlessly and perform major surgery on all that lack the stylistic merits discussed in Section 1.7. Some of the attributes that are regularly revised into technical sentences are:

A. Brevity. Be as brief as possible without being unclear. Many a long sentence benefits by being broken up into several short ones. However, do not make brevity a fetish. Brevity means short words, as well as short sentences: Use the shorter word when you have a choice between words of unequal length, but always use the word that most exactly expresses your meaning, even if it is a long one.

B. Emphasis. Are your sentences, or their parts, equally emphatic, giving the erroneous impression that all of the ideas they express are equally important? Correct any misplaced emphasis: (1) Discard a compound sentence if the subjects of its clauses are not in fact coordinate. (2) Express subordinate ideas with subordinate clauses in complex or compound-complex sentences. (3) Emphasize ideas by tabulating or cataloging them and identifying them with numerals or letters in parentheses, as is done in this paragraph. (4) Use for emphasis any typographical device at your disposal (boldface or italic type, full capitals, underscoring, letter spacing). (5) Use repetition for purposes of emphasis very sparingly: the sophisticated reader likes to think that he can get the message the first time.

C. Consistency. There is an implied contract between writer and reader that compels the former to be uniform in his presentation. If the writer deviates in any way from the course he has led the reader to expect of him, he will confuse the reader. Consistency results from using abbreviations, capitals, symbols, terms, plurals, punctuation, and spelling always in the same way (or carefully explaining any exception). Consistency also means preserving the tone of the report (not talking in one place as if to professional engineers and in another as if to trade school freshmen) and maintaining the style (not being dignified and restrained in one place and flippant and ebullient in another).

A type of inconsistency that slows reading and sometimes causes misunderstanding of the material consists of shifts within a sentence. These include nonparallelism, and shifts of verb tense, verb person, verb mood, point of view, word meaning, and subject.

9.7   PARAGRAPHING

Your rough-draft paragraphs probably will not make much sense structurally. The rewriting of them entails putting the component sentences into proper sequence, adding others to complete the tight structure of a good paragraph, and discarding any extraneous ones.

A good paragraph has a topic sentence. In the paragraph, this sentence is equivalent to the introduction in the report, because it introduces the topic to be discussed. Every thought in the paragraph must relate to this topic (this is *unity*); if one does not, discard the sentence or transfer it to a paragraph where it belongs. The topic sentence usually, but not always, is the first sentence in the paragraph, but it is always somewhere near the beginning. (Sometimes the very first sentence is an introductory one that serves as a transition from the preceding paragraph.) Make your topic sentence clear and strong, and then support it with the sentences that follow. Glue the sentences together with good transitional devices — introductory words or phrases (*Now, Next, For example, However, Moreover, Hence,* and so on) or terminal statements that serve to bridge the gap to the next paragraph ("Next, . . . will be considered," "The following proof is offered," and so on). This is *coherence*. Finally, a paragraph may have an end element — a brief comment, advice, or analysis based upon the paragraph which it summarizes. Note the use of basic elements in the following paragraph:

The slide rule gives no information about any digits in a number beyond those that can be read directly from the scales or that can be approximated with assurance. Moreover, it gives no information about the position of the decimal point in a number. For example, the setting shown in Figure 4-3(*a*) could represent any number whose first three significant digits are, respectively, 1, 3, and 7. Thus it could represent 1.37 or 1,370 or 0.0000137. The placement of the decimal point in the result of a slide-rule computation must be determined separately and from other considerations. It is of the greatest importance, but the slide rule itself gives no help in this.[2]

An analysis of this paragraph reveals the following elements of good structure:

[2]Glade Wilcox and Charles H. Butler, *Industrial Calculating Devices* (New York: Holt, Rinehart and Winston, Inc., 1962), p. 41.

1. Sentence 1 is the topic sentence, and it introduces concretely the central thought of the paragraph.

2. Sentence 2 is introduced by the transitional word *moreover* and augments the idea expressed in the topic sentence.

3. Sentence 3 is introduced by the transitional phrase *for example*, and demonstrates the ideas expressed in sentences 1 and 2.

4. Sentence 4 is introduced by the transitional word *thus*, and illustrates the idea expressed in sentence 3.

5. Sentence 5 states a fact that is reasonably concluded from the evidence presented in sentences 3 and 4.

6. Sentence 6 simultaneously evaluates the thought expressed in sentence 5, relates it to the central topic of the paragraph, and (in summary) rephrases the idea expressed in the topic sentence.

This paragraph thus is a neatly assembled unit. The thoughts in sentences 2 to 6, inclusive, are related to the central thought presented by the topic sentence, No. 1; this gives unity to the paragraph. The use of transitional devices (introductory words in 2 and 4, introductory phrase in 3, introductory pronoun subject *it* in 6, with its referent in the preceding sentence, No. 5) give coherence. The paragraph is free of digressions, unsupported assertion, and deadwood.

Analyze your own paragraphs in the same way, testing for unity, coherence, transitions, topic sentence, and summary statement. Make any corrections, additions, or deletions needed. Although there is nothing sacred about using short paragraphs, be properly critical of long ones; also avoid, if possible, the other extreme — the single-line paragraph.

9.8   RHETORICAL PURPOSE

The discussion section of a report has as its purpose describing, defining, or reviewing — sometimes a combination of two or all of these. Whereas the requirement of language mechanics, style, and tone are the same in each case, the technique of development is somewhat different.

A. Description. In technical reports, this is the depiction of a thing (part, device, machine, instrument, and so on), place, or process. Effective description consists of verbally picturing the subject so clearly that the reader has little or no trouble visualizing it.

Examine your descriptions for a logical development of ideas and sequence of elements. The following outline shows the elements of a device description:

1. Name of device
2. Purpose
3. Over-all characteristics
   a. Size
   b. Weight
   c. Shape
4. Names and functions of parts
   a. Part 1
   b. Part 2
   c. Part *n*
5. Performance
   a. Manipulation
   b. Operation
   c. Maintenance
6. Advantages and disadvantages

In a process description, *steps* replace parts, *procedure* replaces performance, and *method* replaces manipulation.

B. Definition. This is the act of explaining the meaning of something (thing, process, or idea). Unfamiliar items should be defined in terms of familiar ones. The technical writer therefore must avoid vagueness and abstraction. He must also avoid circular definitions (those that go nowhere): not "The X-Y recorder is a kind of *recorder*" but "The X-Y recorder is an *instrument* for . . . ." A brief description will very often reinforce a definition. Note the interplay of naming and elucidating in the following definition:

TRANSDUCERS. Any device which converts one form of energy into another form is called a *transducer*. For example, a thermocouple transforms heat energy into electrical energy and is, therefore, called a transducer. Other familiar transducers include: microphones, which convert sound into electrical energy; strain gauges to convert tension or stress into electrical energy; and accelerometers, which convert acceleration into electrical energy.[3]

When the report contains a number of special terms, or familiar words used in a special way, a glossary of such terms (which is a brief dictionary) should be included in the report (see Section 2.1C, part 17). Any new or unusual term must be defined, usually in parentheses, when it first appears in the report; after that, the reader is expected to be familiar with it:

[3]Jacob H. Ruiter, Jr., and R. Gordon Murphy, *Basic Industrial Electronic Controls* (New York: Holt, Rinehart and Winston, Inc., 1961), p. 9.

Better impact strength is provided by Oleform TD-228 (a reinforced polypropylene plastic).

C. Review. Progress reports generally review work that has been performed. The work may be any form of physical or mental activity from building hardware to searching literature. A review thus is an account of some activity.

The technique for reviewing is governed by the demands of the reporting situation. A review of progress on a work project, for example, commonly employs the past tense of verbs, since it recounts activities that occurred at a former time. It is generally arranged chronologically ("This was done first, this next," and so on). Therefore this type of review is one of the few instances of narration to be found in a technical report. But a review of the findings from a literature search, investigation, or survey is usually presented in the present tense ("The balloon is at home at altitudes that are too high for aircraft and too low for satellites."). Only when the researcher must discuss the act of investigation is the past tense required ("The *Industrial Arts Index* for 1958 was consulted.").

9.9   ORGANIZATION

The outline is the skeleton of organization, and the various drafts of the report need only to be checked against it for agreement, and made to agree if they differ. If a stylebook or report specification has been followed, however, the organization of the report must be checked against the format prescribed by that source.

The parts of the report, and each block of supporting material in each part, should be clearly identified by headings and subheads. The main headings and most of the subheads can come directly from the report parts list or from the outline (see Sections 2.1B, 2.2B, and 2.3B). Sometimes special ones must be written. The heading and subhead, like the caption of an illustration, must be a brief title of the passage it identifies. Observe that the material in this book is separated into main and subordinate sections, each of which is labeled with a numbered or lettered heading or subhead.

There is no set format for the organization of main and subordinate material and for the headings and subheads designating this material. Some writers follow a format prescribed by a stylebook; others work out a plan of their own in collaboration with their editors. When the report is to be letterpress printed, a suitable style may be planned in consultation with the printer, and may use capitals, lower case, and different type faces to express the various degrees of coordination and subordination. When restricted to typewriter type, however, the writer will find the format shown in Figure 9-1

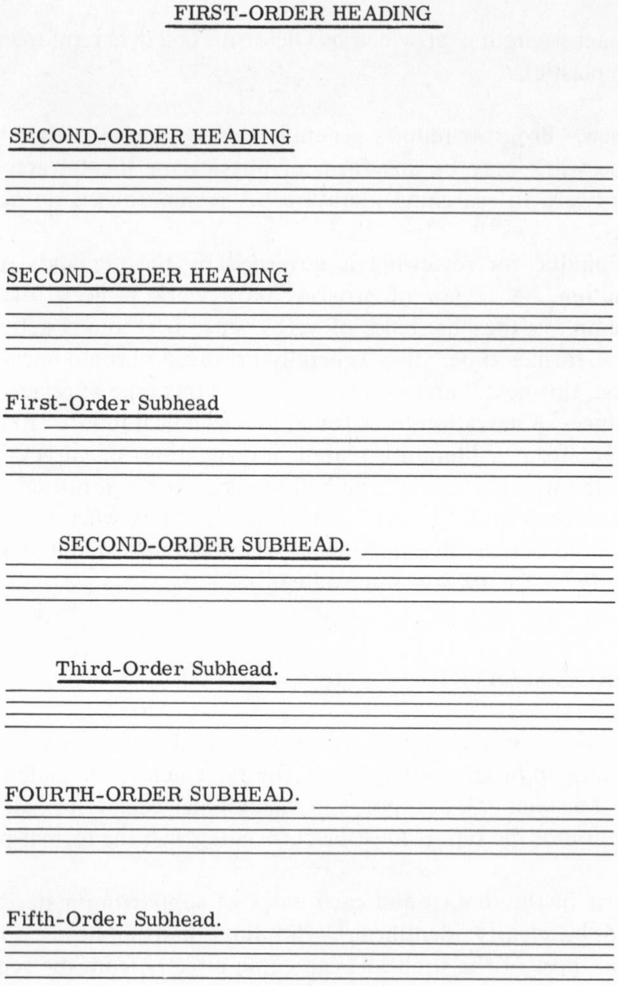

FIRST-ORDER HEADING

SECOND-ORDER HEADING

SECOND-ORDER HEADING

First-Order Subhead

SECOND-ORDER SUBHEAD.

Third-Order Subhead.

FOURTH-ORDER SUBHEAD.

Fifth-Order Subhead.

Fig. 9-1   Format for Headings and Subheads.

serviceable. Observe closely the use of capitals, lower case, periods, under-
lining, and indentation in this layout. Here, the first-order heading is *cen-
tered;* the second-order headings are *flush, hanging* (that is, starting flush with
the left-hand margin of the page and hanging above the text); the first-order
subhead is *flush, hanging;* the second- and third-order subheads are *indented,
run-in* (that is, moved in from the margin and run in with the text); and the
fourth- and fifth-order subheads are *flush, run-in*. In the copy under the subheads (and second-order headings), all lines after the first start flush with the
left-hand margin of the page. All indentations are five spaces in from the
left-hand margin of the page.

Headings and subheads are numbered (or lettered, or both) in some reports, unnumbered in others. This is a matter of preference, but the usage must be consistent. Note that they are numbered (corresponding to the letter-number outline form) in the specimen student report in Appendix 2, and unnumbered in the specimen professional reports in Appendix 4 and Appendix 6 and in the specimen laboratory test report in Appendix 5.

Considerable rewriting time can be saved whenever material is found to be in the wrong place but in no need of revision, simply by cutting the entire passage out and pasting it where it belongs. There is no need to copy it. Throughout the revision phase, a pair of scissors and a jar of rubber cement or roll of Scotch tape are as useful as a typewriter or pen.

9.10 FOOTNOTING

Footnotes are usually found only in a few formal reports, being more common to articles, books, and scholarly papers. They are invaluable when needed, but should never be used for mere padding. A footnote gives information, such as an explanatory note or reference to a supporting article or book, that would obstruct the reading if it appeared in the text. A footnote should appear at the bottom of the page to which it applies and should be separated from the last line of the text on the page by means of a single line drawn long enough to isolate the footnote. (Some printed works omit this "hairline" rule; to secure isolation, they use a smaller type face in the footnote than that used in the text.) The practice of placing all footnotes in the back of the report is to be discouraged, since this compels the reader to make trips back and forth between text and back matter and can seriously slow the reading and interpretation.

Attention is called to a footnote by means of a superscript (exponent), usually placed at the end of the sentence containing the topic to be footnoted — as here.[4] Number the footnote with the same superscript, and use the numbers consecutively. Note the style of footnote 4, below, and of the other footnotes in this chapter. A footnote referring to an article or book must contain (1) name of author(s), (2) name of publication, (3) facts of publication (city of publication and name of publisher if a book, name of journal or magazine and sometimes its volume number, and date of publication), and (4) page number. An informational footnote simply contains a brief statement of the supplementary information, as in footnote 4, below.

When reference is later made to a footnote, the latter need not be completely rewritten in the new place. For footnote 3 in this chapter, for example, a subsequent citation would be simply

[4]Ibid., p. 207.

[4]The superscript in the footnote, as here, is indented. The first line starts immediately after, and each additional line starts flush with the left-hand margin.

if the new footnote appears on the same page or a facing page and no other footnotes come between. If there are intervening footnotes or pages, *ibid.* cannot be used; the abbreviated footnote then is

[4]Ruiter and Murphy, *op. cit.*, p. 207.

The abbreviation for a *full* repetition of the footnote (author, publication, page number, and passage on the page) is

[4]Ruiter and Murphy, *loc. cit.*

If this footnote comes right after the original one, it may be simplified to

[4]*Loc. cit.*

These are Latin abbreviations; *ibid.* = *ibidem* = "in the same place," *op. cit.* = *opere citato* = "in the work cited," and *loc. cit.* = *loco citato* = "in the place cited." Writers who do not favor the Latin terms use shortened English footnotes:

[4]Ruiter and Murphy, p. 207.
or
[4]*Basic Industrial Electronic Controls*, p. 207.

For a more exhaustive treatment of footnoting, see Robert M. Schmitz, *Preparing the Research Paper* (New York: Holt, Rinehart and Winston, Inc., 1959), pp. 47–52.

EXERCISES

9.1 Revise and rewrite the following rough-draft sentences:

(*a*) The selection of the consulting firm was based according to Marshall on their ability to formulate the program practical-wise.

(*b*) Working under a contract from Space Research Associates, a new set of trajectory equations were worked out which an inexperienced engineer can follow if you have had only introductory calculus.

(*c*) Pure nickel powder consisting of loose dendritic agglomerates of 99.9% pure nickel particles can be used in fuel cells, strong 90 percent porosity compacts can be prepared with it.

(*d*) Four chemists examined the substance; they work first on the assumption that it is galena and applied several preliminary quick tests which show that it isn't.

9.2 The following paragraph lacks coherence. Rewrite it, supplying the transitional devices it needs.

General Electric Co. is working on a "pedipulator." This is a combination human-mechanical walking machine. The work is being done under an Army contract. A man will be inside the pedipulator. Ultimately, the machine will imitate every movement of the man as he "walks" the machine over obstacles or makes it do lifting, just as if he were walking or working unaided. The power of his own arms and legs will be amplified by the mechanism. He will be able to perform many feats which are impossible with his relatively weak arms and legs alone. The man will be sensitive, through a feedback system, to the "sensations" and movements of the machine. The pedipulator will be equivalent to a robot with nerves and brain supplied by the man inside.

9.3 Using the list of references on page 13 of the specimen student report (Appendix 2), compose a series of footnotes for the report, indicating the points at which the footnotes will be called out. If a footnote need be referred to more than once, use the scheme of abbreviating given in Section 9.10.

9.4 Write a description of a log-log duplex decitrig slide rule (see the description outline in Section 9.8A).

9.5 Write a definition of any instrument or process from your major technical field. Test your definition against the requirements given in Section 9.8B.

10

Preparing the Final Draft

Work in the final drafting phase is largely mechanical, but it is no mere routine step in the production of the report; all of the assiduousness that characterizes revision and rewriting is required in preparing the final draft. Here, the final draft is made ready for the reader or the reproducer, and this is the last chance to correct mistakes, polish the writing, and systematize the structure.

In order for the work of final drafting to proceed smoothly, all report material must be available by the time this work is started. Virtually all of the material will be completely revised by this time, but this does not prevent still further modification during the process of final drafting.

Depending upon the type of report, method of reproduction, and stratification of the issuing organization, the work of final drafting might be done by writer, editor, or both. In any case, final drafting is as much a part of the writing as any of the earlier phases.

For inspection, the final draft of a professional report is reproduced in Appendix 6.

10.1   STEPS IN THE PROCESS

The amount and kind of final work required and the steps needed to complete it depend upon the type, kind, and length of report. A formal report requires more work than an informal one, and a long formal report more than a short one. Also, a report that is to be letterpress printed needs more final work than one which will be mimeographed. The steps and procedure discussed in Sections 10.2 to 10.13, inclusive, are those followed in the final drafting of a formal report in the order in which they appear here. At the other extreme is the informal report of the letter or memorandum type, which requires only a final check for completeness, accuracy, unity, coherence, and polish, and a possible final rewrite.

104

10.2   ASSEMBLING MATERIAL

This step is the gathering together of *all* material which has been prepared or collected in the preceding phases, and the consolidation of this material. This includes revised draft, illustrations, and supplementary matter. Set a firm deadline for the delivery of such material and the filing of approvals of it.

Prepare the last version of the report by (1) fitting all of the material together, each item in its proper place, and (2) writing the final draft from it. As in the organizational revision (Section 9.9), scissors and rubber cement or Scotch tape are indispensable here when entire passages must be shifted from one place to another more logical one.

10.3   FORMAT

The format, initially prescribed or earlier agreed upon, must be followed closely here. Fit the revised material into the plan of the report (see report parts in Sections 2.1C, 2.2B, and 2.3B). Shift material into proper places when its position runs contrary to the outline.

Maintain the systematic arrangement of material into principal and subordinate sections identified by the various orders of headings and sub-heads (see Section 9.9 and Figure 9-1). If final readings show any material to be out of place in any of these sections, create a new section for it and subordinate and label this section appropriately.

The original format is not necessarily final; it can be changed in this final phase of production if the need for a more effective organization is apparent.

10.4   PLACEMENT OF ILLUSTRATIONS

Illustrations were selected or placed on order during preliminary planning, and they were captioned and referred to as early as the rough-drafting phase. Now is the time to insert, or direct the insertion of, these illustrations into the report itself. Although this is a job normally performed by the editor, whose function is to manufacture a report from the written material supplied by the writer, the latter sometimes must do this work.

If the report is to be letterpress or photo-offset printed, the editor or writer will paste proofs of the illustrations into the copy during the dummying of pages (Section 10.13C). If, instead, the report is to be reproduced by one of the other methods, the illustrations must be pasted, or drawn, onto the pages of the final draft itself.

Insert an illustration as close as practicable to the point at which it is first mentioned. Often, it is difficult to get very close to the point when there are many illustrations to be fitted in; in such a case, the illustration should be placed after, never before, the mention. This spares the reader from turning back in the report.

When there is a single small illustration, place it at the center of the page, with copy above and below it, as shown in Figure 10-1(*a*). If placing an il-

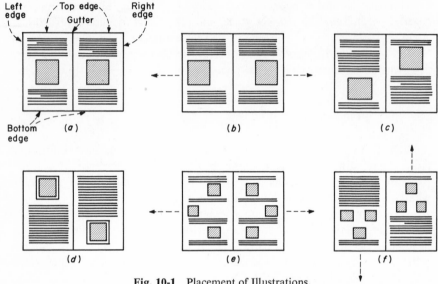

Fig. 10-1 Placement of Illustrations.

lustration at the very top or bottom of a page is unavoidable, however, allow at least two or three lines of copy above the top-of-page illustration and below the bottom-of-page one (see Figure 10-1*c*). If no copy at all is available for this purpose, box the illustration in a bold frame, as shown in Figure 10-1*d*, to prevent it from bleeding off the page. Avoid placing an illustration at the outer edge of a page (Figure 10-1*b*), as this positioning tends to lead the reader's eye off the page in the direction of the arrow.

When several illustrations must be placed on one page, group them, if possible, in such a way that they create no distracting pattern. For example, avoid groupings which form a pointer that guides the eye off the page. This is what happens in Figure 10-1(*e*) and (*f*), where the eye is led off the page in the direction of the arrows. It would be better to group the illustrations along the gutter, if possible, since this keeps the reader's eye on the page.

A single large illustration will require a full page without copy. Following standard procedure, position these illustrations so that their tops are to the left as the report lies open. This will place the caption along the gutter on the left-hand page and along the outer edge on the right-hand page (see

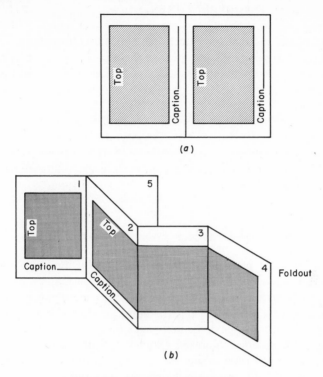

Fig. 10-2 Placement of Illustrations.

Figure 10-2*a*). If there is no room for the caption in these places, put it along the lower edge of either page (Figure 10-2(*b*), left-hand side of the drawing).

Large illustrations more than a page in size must be folded to fit them into the report. This is shown in Figure 10-2(*b*), right-hand side of the drawing. Practice differs in the numbering of such a foldout. As shown in Figure 10-2(*b*), some editors number each page-wide section so that three pages (2, 3, and 4) would be represented by this foldout, and the next text page would be No. 5. Others call the entire foldout one page, and would number the next text page in this example No. 3. Whichever method you choose, be consistent in using it.

In each of the foregoing examples, artwork has been assumed, so the convention has been observed of placing the caption below the illustration. If the illustration were a chart or table, the caption would be placed above it (see Section 8.9).

Check the copy for references to the illustrations. When you must change the number of an illustration, correct the number in every reference to that illustration *throughout* the report.

10.5   HANDLING APPENDIXES

Complete and number (or letter) each appendix (for example, *Appendix 6*, *Appendix VI*, *Appendix F*) and arrange them consecutively by number or letter. Identify each appendix by means of a brief title, in addition to the number or letter:

APPENDIX 2. Pneumatic Transmission Systems

Check the copy for references to the appendixes. When you must change the number of an appendix, correct the number in every reference to that appendix *throughout* the report.

10.6   PAGINATION

Number the text pages consecutively with Arabic numerals. This final numbering will replace any temporary pagination you may have been using with the various revisions. The usual place for a page number is the upper left-hand corner of a left-hand page, the upper right-hand corner of a right-hand page, and lower center of the first page of a chapter. There is considerable variation in practice, however. Sometimes all pages in a report are numbered at the lower right (when the report is reproduced on one side of sheets only, so that all pages are therefore right-hand ones). All pages in the specimen student report (Appendix 2) are numbered at lower center, and those in the specimen professional report (Appendix 4) and the specimen final draft (Appendix 6) are numbered at the lower left corner of left-hand pages, and lower right corner of right-hand pages.

Number the front-matter pages with lower-case Roman numerals (*i*, *ii*, *iii*, *iv*, *v*, . . .) positioned according to one of the schemes explained in the preceding paragraph, consistent with the number positioning in the rest of the report. The title page is the first page of the report and has the front-matter number *i*, but no number actually appears on that page. Back-matter pages continue the numbering from the main text.

When the report has a large number of pages, consecutive page numbering introduces a proportionately large chance of error; if one page has accidentally been misnumbered, or an additional page must be inserted, the numbers of many pages must be corrected from that point to the end of the report. Also, every reference to those pages must be painstakingly located and corrected throughout the report. To circumvent this emergency, separate pagination sometimes is used in the chapters or sections of a long report. In this scheme, the page number has two parts. The first part is the chapter number, and the second is the page number in that chapter; thus,

3-10 or III-10 is page 10 in Chapter 3, whereas 7-10 or VII-10 is page 10 in Chapter 7. With this system, numbers need be changed only from a correction point to the end of the chapter.

A bound-in photograph is generally considered a page and is so numbered. A foldout illustration may be numbered as one or several pages [see Section 10.4 and Figure 10-2(*b*)].

10.7   END WRITING

There are some parts of the report which cannot very well be written until all information is final and the pagination is complete. These parts, which should be composed in rough draft and carried through as many revisions as necessary, are:

1. Abstract or summary (Section 2.1C, part 11)
2. Letter of transmittal (Section 2.1C, part 4)
3. Acknowledgments (Section 2.1C, part 8)
4. Preface or foreword (Section 2.1C, part 7)
5. Glossary (Section 2.1C, part 17)
6. Index (Section 2.1C, part 19)
7. Table of contents (Section 2.1C, part 9)

All of this material is front matter and is paginated with lower-case Roman numerals as explained in Section 10.6. Note that acknowledgments are combined with the foreword on page *ii* of the specimen professional report in Appendix 6.

10.8   PROTECTION

Safeguards, either governmental or private, are applied to many reports. It is the responsibility of writer and editor to see that they are observed. Common ones are listed below.

A. Security Classification. If the report is confidential, secret, or top secret, this classification must be conspicuously displayed at the top and bottom of each page and the cover. The word is printed in bold capitals. If you have no preprinted pages inscribed in this manner, and are limited to typewriter type, letterspace the word for conspicuousness when you type it at the top and bottom of each page.

B. Espionage Statement. Some reports to government agencies are required to carry an *espionage statement*. This must appear in the prescribed words and on the prescribed page (cover, title page, or special front-matter page, as required). Do not change the wording of the statement as it is given by the agency.

C. Clearances. To protect its right to proprietary information, a company or organization may prohibit the publication of any document, including a report, without prior approval by designated officials. As evidence that this approval has been obtained, a page must be provided for the signatures of all persons who have the authority to clear the report. (This may be the same as the approvals page discussed in Section 2.1C, part 5.)

The usual clearance authorities in an industrial concern are the (1) legal department, (2) patent department, (3) public relations department, and (4) advertising department.

D. Copyright. Some reports issued by private agencies are copyrighted. In a large company, the legal department will handle this matter, but the writer or editor must reserve three copies of the published report to be filed with the application for copyright. The writer must also see to it that the conventional copyright page is provided in the final draft. This immediately follows the title page and contains the copyright notice (for example, *Copyright* © 1964 *by ABC Space Systems, Inc.*). Also see the copyright page of this book.

A copyright protects only the literary content of the report, as a safeguard against plagiarism; it provides no protection for inventions or processes described therein. Therefore, do not expect a copyright to perform the same function as a patent — at a considerably lower cost.

10.9   TITLING

The title of a report may be prescribed by a work contract (for example, *Final Progress Report, Jupiter IX Booster Development*) or it may be self-evident (for example, *Strength of Materials Laboratory Report No. 11*). In a great many cases, however, the title must be worked out, and the final drafting phase is the proper time for composing it, because the report is then complete and its *actual* coverage distinct for the first time.

Make your title as truthful as you possibly can. Be as brief as clarity and accuracy will allow. (See Section 2.1C, part 1.) Add a subtitle if necessary. Avoid titles that ask questions (for example, *Is a Traffic Tunnel Under San Francisco Bay Feasible?*). Note the titles of the specimen final report in Appendix 6, the student report in Appendix 2, the professional report in Appendix 4, and the laboratory test report in Appendix 5.

10.10   TITLE PAGE

The title page bears the title of the report and any other information needed to describe, identify, and categorize it: serial number, contract number, name of recipient, name of issuing organization, address of organization. See Section 2.1C, parts 2 and 3, for typical details.

Note that the specimen professional report in Appendix 6 contains, in addition to the title, the name of the contracting agency with a complete breakdown, the name of the issuing organization with a complete breakdown, the address of the issuing organization, the author's name, the author's title and address, the contract number, the project number, and the task number. Note also similar information on the title page of the professional report in Appendix 4, and compare with this the comparatively simple title page of the student report in Appendix 2.

10.11   COVERS

The front cover contains most, and sometimes all, of the information appearing on the title page (see Section 2.1C, part 2). The inside front cover, inside back cover, and outside back cover are usually blank, but occasionally the distribution list is printed on the inside front cover.

Note that the report in Appendix 6 and the ones in Appendixes 2 and 4 use their title pages as front covers. Note also that the first and third of these display company insignia on their front covers.

Release your cover plans to illustrators immediately after they are settled, if artwork is required. This will insure that they will be ready when needed.

10.12   PREPARATION FOR REPRODUCTION

Your report most likely will be issued in more than one copy. The method of its reproduction will govern the form of the final draft. The final report in Appendix 6, for example, is satisfactory for direct reproduction from its pages by means of Xerox or photocopy. It has undergone final typing and pasting-in of illustrations. A matrix for offset reproduction (for example, Multilith) could also be made photographically from its pages. If this report were to be reproduced by letterpress printing, a neatly typed manuscript without illustrations would be sufficient.

A. Letterpress. Type final draft, double-spaced and on one side of sheet, for printer. Place no illustrations on these pages. Make cuts of all illustrations.

B. Multilith. Type final draft, and transfer illustrations, onto paper masters (a special ribbon and pencil must be used), or photograph final draft and its pasted-in illustrations onto metal masters. Have special masters made of photographs.

C. Mimeograph. Type final draft and make line drawings on stencils. No ribbon is needed, and special styli must be used for drawing.

D. Xerox. Type final draft and paste in illustrations. (Line drawings can be made directly on the page, if desired, but photographs must be pasted in.)

E. Ozalid. Type final draft, and make line drawings, on vellum (tracing paper) sheets. Use a backing sheet of carbon paper to give additional impression on back of sheet.

F. Ditto. Type final draft, and make line drawings, on paper masters. No special ribbon or styli are needed.

10.13   PRINTING DEMANDS

Letterpress printing has been called the queen of the reproduction processes. It well deserves the title, because a printed report is far superior in appearance and legibility to any other. However, this process is the most expensive and it demands a good amount of work by the writer/editor after the report has been reduced to a final typescript.

A. Marking Copy for Printer. The final typescript to be sent to a printer for setting in type must be properly marked to show the desired face and size of type, required spacing, and other mechanical details — directions to the printer. This is a highly specialized art which cannot be fully explained in this text. Furthermore, it requires considerable experience. If you are unskilled in the marking of copy, turn the final draft over to an editor who is proficient in this work; or if such a one is unavailable, obtain the service from the printer's staff.

B. Proofreading. After the type has been set, the printer will supply galley proofs of this material, and you must read them carefully, for mistakes, against your copy of the draft. Use standard proofreading marks for indicating any corrections (see Figure 10-3). Do your writing in the margins of the proofs (see Figure 10-4). If time permits, have another reader check your work.

By all means, make every necessary correction. But remember that printing alterations are costly, so avoid making changes simply because you have thought of a more elegant way of saying something.

C. Dummying Pages. After the mistakes have been corrected by the printer and approved by you, you will receive a set of clean, corrected galley proofs for use in making dummy pages. You will also receive a proof of each illustration cut.

A page is dummied by pasting copy, clipped from the appropriate galley proof, and cut proofs, on a sheet of paper within an area identical with that of the intended size of the printed report page. The operation is not as easy as it sounds; it requires a great deal of careful measurement and a good sense of proportion and balancing. An experienced editor should do this

Fig. 10-3   Standard Proofreading Marks.

work, but a few technical writers (especially those in one-man departments) become proficient at it. Handle the job if you can.

Following your dummies, the print shop will combine the specified type and cuts into pages and will submit proofs of them for your inspection.

This is your second proofreading task. Read the page proofs carefully. Make any necessary corrections, but shun any change which is unessential — alterations are very expensive at this point.

It does not appear that the earliest printers had any method of correcting errors before the form was on the press. The learned correctors of the first two centuries of printing were not proofreaders in our sense; they were rather what we should term office editors. Their labors were chiefly to see that the proof corresponded to the copy, but that the printed page was correct in its latinity—that the words were there, and that the sense was right. They cared little about orthography, bad letters, or purely printers' errors, and when the text seemed to them wrong they consulted fresh authorities or altered it on their own responsibility. Good proofs in the modern sense were impossible until professional readers were employed, men who had first a printer's education, and then spent many years in the correction of proof. The orthography of English, which for the past century has undergone little change, was very fluctuating until after the publication of Johnson's Dictionary, and capitals, which have been used with considerable regularity for the past 80 years, were previously used on the miss or hit plan. The approach to regularity, so far as we have, may be attributed to the growth of a class of professional proofreaders, and it is to them that we owe the correctness of modern printing. More errors have been found in the Bible than in any other one work. For many generations it was frequently the case that Bibles were brought out stealthily, from fear of governmental interference. They were frequently printed from imperfect texts, and were often modified to meet the views of those who published them. The story is related that a certain woman in Germany, the wife of a printer, and had become disgusted with the continual assertions of the superiority of man over woman which she had heard, hurried into the composing room while her husband was at supper and altered a sentence in the Bible, which he was printing, so that it read "Narr" instead of "Herr," thus making the verse read "And he shall be thy fool" instead of "and he shall be they lord." The word not was omitted by Barker, the king's printer in England in 1632, in printing the seventh commandment. He was fined £3,000 on this account.

Fig. 10-4. Sample of Marked Proof.

APPENDIX 1

Specimen Memorandum Report

BRADY AND WOOD

To Michael Wood
Vice President

Date June 22, 1964

From Carl Wood
Environmental Test Laboratory

Ref Contract No.
A-7376

Subject Test of Kentex Insulating Tape

The following table gives physical and electrical properties
of Kentex insulating tape as measured in our environmental
test laboratory. These data are average values calculated
from figures obtained by testing samples from 100 rolls of
tape. The individual figures will be found in Laboratory
Notebook No. 164, pages 15 to 28, inclusive.

BRITTLENESS TEMPERATURE	Less than $-35^{o}C$
COEFFICIENT OF FRICTION	0.40
COLOR	Colorless, transparent
DIELECTRIC STRENGTH (1.5-mil strip) 60 cps	1000 v/mil
DROP TEST (Dart Drop) 1.5-mil strip, 50% failure	200 gm/mil
ELONGATION (machine direction)	220 %
ELONGATION (transverse direction)	315 %
MOISTURE ABSORPTION (24 hr test)	0.10 %
SPECIFIC GRAVITY	1.1
TEAR STRENGTH-ELMENDORF (machine direction) (transverse direction)	240 gm/mil 230 gm/mil
TENSILE YIELD STRENGTH (machine direction)	2000 psi
TENSILE YIELD STRENGTH (transverse direction)	2140 psi

This is the information you requested (6/15/64) for our client, the Gray Corporation.

Carl West

Laboratory Notebook Ref: Book No. 164, pp. 15-28

CW:ald

cc: J. Brady

APPENDIX 2

Specimen Student Report

OPERATION OF SEMICONDUCTOR DIODE

AS A VARISTOR

By

Guy Dexter, Jr.

California State College at Los Angeles

A term report submitted in partial fulfillment
of the requirements of English 306,
Technical Report Writing

California State College at L. A.
Los Angeles, California 90032
June 1, 1964

Prof. Rufus P. Turner
Department of English
Calif. State College at L. A.

Dear Sir:

Attached is one copy of my report, <u>Operation of Semicon-</u>
<u>ductor Diode as a Varistor,</u> submitted in partial ful-
fillment of the requirements of your course, English
306, Technical Report Writing.

Very truly yours,

Guy Dexter Jr.

GDJr: ms   Guy Dexter, Jr.

 Attach: One copy of report

TABLE OF CONTENTS

SUMMARY

A semiconductor diode may be used under certain conditions as a simple, inexpensive dc-controlled variable resistor. Tests described in this report indicate that a resistance change of 600 to 1 can be obtained by varying the forward current of a typical 1N34A germanium diode from 1 microampere to 30 milliamperes. The results appear promising, but additional conductance tests should be performed on silicon diodes and on power-type semiconductor rectifiers. Also, a study should be made of the effects of acceleration, altitude, humidity, magnetism, radiation, and vibration on varistor action.

OPERATION OF SEMICONDUCTOR DIODE AS A VARISTOR

I. INTRODUCTION

A varistor is a resistor whose resistance depends upon
applied voltage or current. The resistance of this component
therefore may be varied by adjusting the current or voltage
level. When a variable direct current already is available
in a circuit, it may be used to vary the resistance of a varistor automatically for such purposes as tuning, modulation,
amplitude stabilization, tube or transistor biasing, or voltage regulation. If such a current is absent, one may be introduced from the outside for frequency correction, curve
changing, amplitude setting, or remote tuning.

Because they are two-terminal devices, varistors are
simple in structure and installation. Various kinds have
been used in electronic circuits, and include silicon carbide elements, thermistors, and incandescent-lamp fila-
ments (1, 2). But whereas these types scarcely resemble
each other, they have one feature in common: nonohmic
performance, i.e., in them E/I is not a constant.

-1-

From a previous experiment, it seemed likely that a small-signal semiconductor diode might be usable as a varistor of significant resistance range if it were dc-biased in the forward direction (i.e., anode positive, cathode negative), since the volt-ampere characteristic of such a diode is known to be nonlinear. Commercially available diodes use copper oxide, gallium arsenide, germanium, selenium, or silicon as the semiconductor material. However, this report presents experimental data obtained through d-c measurements on a germanium diode only. The germanium type was chosen because it is inexpensive, common, and small. Moreover, a large quantity was available for testing. The results of the tests show that the diode can serve as a varistor.

Topics discussed in this report are (1) applicable properties of the germanium diode selected, (2) measurement of the forward E-I characteristic, (3) extent of the dc-variable resistance, (4) advantages and disadvantages of the diode as a varistor, and (5) recommendations for further work.

II. DISCUSSION

A. Germanium Diode Test Sample

Hughes Type 1N34A germanium diode was tested. This
is a general-purpose, small-signal, point-contact diode
rated at minimum 1-volt forward current of 5 milliamperes
dc at 25°C. The 1N34A is small (0.019 inch in diameter
and 0.3 inch long), inexpensive (43 cents from 1 to 99,
32 cents in larger lots), and has 1-inch pigtails for
easy wiring. One hundred diodes were tested.

B. Test Procedure

Only the forward conduction characteristic of the
diode was checked, the reverse characteristic being of
no interest. The procedure consisted of adjusting the
forward current (independent variable, I_f) through each
diode successively to each of 28 values from 1 microampere to 30 milliamperes, and reading the corresponding
forward voltage drop (dependent variable, E_f) across
the diode.

Figure 1 shows the test circuit. In this arrangement, B is a dry battery (Burgess Type 4FM 1½-v cell for
currents up to 1 ma, Burgess Type 4F4H 6-v battery for

currents from 2 to 30 ma), R a rheostat consisting of three
Cornell-Dubilier resistance decade boxes (Type RDA, RDB,
and RDC) connected in series to permit a resistance variation

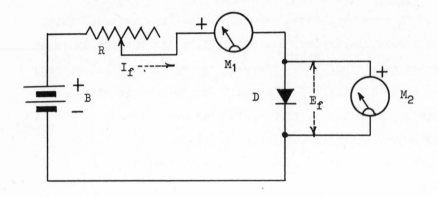

FIGURE 1. TEST CIRCUIT

from 1 ohm to 1,111,110 ohms in 1-ohm steps, M_1 a multirange
d-c meter (Simpson Model 260 switched to its 100-μa, 10-ma,
or 100-ma range, as required), D the diode under test, and
M_2 a d-c vacuum-tube voltmeter (Triplett Model 850 switched
to its 0.5-v, 1.5-v, or 5-v range, as required). The high
input resistance of the v-t voltmeter promotes accuracy
through minimum loading of the diode. With its input
resistance of 11 megohms, this instrument draws only 0.2
microampere at the highest diode voltage (2.25 v) and 0.004
microampere at the lowest diode voltage (0.045 v). Such
current drain is negligible.

Setting the six selector switches of the resistor decades (R) permitted adjustment of the forward current (I_f) smoothly to the following successive values: 1, 5, 10, 20, 30, 40, 50, 60, 70, 80, 90, 100, 200, 300, 400, and 500 microamperes; and 1, 2, 3, 4, 5, 6, 7, 8, 9, 10, 20, and 30 milliamperes. The corresponding forward voltage drops (E_f) were easily read on the $6\frac{1}{2}$-inch scale of v-t voltmeter M_2. All measurements were made at an ambient temperature of approximately $25^{\circ}C$.

C. Test Data

The current flowing through the PN junction at the point of contact in the diode is complex. Shea (3) gives the following expression for this current at room temperature:

$$I = I_o \ (exp \ 39 \ V - 1) \tag{1}$$

where I = junction current,
I_o= saturation current of junction, and
V = voltage across junction.

Forward current increases rapidly in response to voltage shifts about a very low mean voltage. For instance, a

2:1 voltage change from 0.1 v produces a 14:1 current
change in a typical 1N34A diode. At successively
higher mean voltages, however, the slope of the E-I
curve becomes less steep, eventually approaching lin-
earity (thus, a 2:1 voltage change from 1 v produces
only 3:1 current change). It means the same to say
that the voltage drop across the diode increases more
slowly than the current flowing through the diode. The
nonlinear current-voltage relationship suggests significant dependence of forward resistance (E_f/I_f) upon
current level.

From the individual measurements, forward conduction curves were plotted to show highest, lowest, and
average performance (see Figure 2).

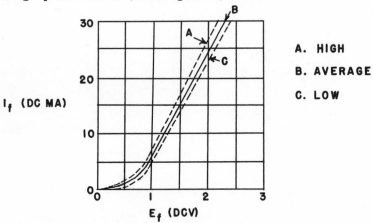

A. HIGH

B. AVERAGE

C. LOW

FIGURE 2.   FORWARD CONDUCTION CHARACTERISTIC

Table 1 (first two columns) shows the test data for a diode of average performance (solid curve in Figure 2). Corresponding resistance values are given in the third column.

TABLE 1. DIODE CONDUCTION DATA

I_f	E_f	R_f
1 μa	0.045 v	45,000 Ω
5	0.100	20,000
10	0.120	12,000
20	0.145	7250
30	0.160	5340
40	0.175	4370
50	0.185	3700
60	0.195	3250
70	0.205	2930
80	0.208	2600
90	0.210	2330
100	0.219	2190
200	0.255	1275
300	0.290	966
400	0.320	800
500	0.341	682
1 ma	0.435	435
2	0.560	280
3	0.670	223
4	0.760	190
5	0.850	170
6	0.920	153
7	1.00	143
8	1.06	132
9	1.12	124
10	1.20	120
20	1.80	90
30	2.25	75

The resistance values are calculated:

$$R_f = E_f/I_f \qquad (2)$$

And it should be noted that here R_f is static resistance.
Dynamic resistance (dE_f/dI_f) is lower in every instance.

D. Observations

From the test data (Figure 2, Table 1), the following
performance is noted:

1. Forward voltage increases nonlinearly
with forward current.

2. A portion of the forward conduction
curve is approximately square law (see
Figure 2).

3. Static forward resistance varies inversely with forward current.

4. Static forward resistance of a typical (average-performance) 1N34A diode at
room temperature $(25^{\circ}C)$ decreases from
45 kilohms at 1 microampere to 75 ohms
at 30 milliamperes.

E. Advantages

As a dc-variable resistor, the 1N34A diode offers several advantages:

1. Small size (0.019" D, 0.3" L)

2. Two-terminal simplicity

3. Instantaneous action

4. Low shunt capacitance (1 pf maximum

5. Wide resistance range (600:1 for current change from 1 μa to 30 ma)

6. Low cost (43 cents)

7. Easy availability

But the diode also has some disadvantages.

F. Disadvantages

1. Relatively low current-handling ability (50 ma maximum)

2. Asymmetry. (Diode is intended to be

a rectifier, therefore exhibits uni-
lateral conductivity and must be poled
correctly for _forward_ current flow.)

3. Temperature sensitivity. (Causes
resistance to vary inversely with
temperature.)

4. Restricted signal amplitude.
(The peak voltage of an a-c signal
superimposed upon the d-c control
current must be small with respect
to the d-c voltage drop across the
diode; otherwise, it will shift the
diode resistance. Roughly, the peak
signal amplitude should not exceed
one-tenth of the d-c voltage.)

III. CONCLUSIONS

Type 1N34A point-contact germanium diode appears to
be satisfactory for use as a simple, inexpensive, low-
powered, current-controlled varistor. Average performance
indicates that its resistance may be varied from 75 ohms

to 45 kilohms by reducing its forward current from 30 milliamperes to 1 microampere.

No measurements were made at elevated temperature. but it is well known that, for a given current, diode voltage drop and resistance decrease as temperature increases (4). And it is also well known that temperature effects are more severe in germanium than in silicon. This would suggest that the germanium diode-type varistor might have limited utility outside of a constant-temperature environment.

IV. RECOMMENDATIONS

Additional investigation is recommended. In this connection, the following lines of study seem appropriate:

A. Test the 1N34A germanium diode over the temperature range -40°C to +100°C.

B. Completely test small-signal silicon junction diodes with a view to exploiting the better temperature coefficient of silicon.

C. Completely test silicon power rectifiers for the higher current and voltage they can handle.

D. Test pairs of diodes or rectifiers
connected in parallel-opposite polarity
for a-c varistor action.

E. Study the effects on the varistor
of acceleration, altitude, humidity,
magnetism, radiation, and vibration.

REFERENCES

1. Anon. "Non-Linear Resistors," <u>Aerovox Research Worker</u>, October-November 1953 (Aerovox Corporation, New Bedford, Massachusetts).

2. Patchett, N. G. "Precision A.C. Voltage Stabilizers," <u>Electronic Engineering</u>, September 1950, p. 371.

3. Shea, Richard F. <u>Principles of Transistor Circuits</u>. New York: John Wiley & Sons, Inc., 1953, p. 8.

4. Turner, Rufus P. <u>Semiconductor Devices</u>. New York: Holt, Rinehart and Winston, Inc., 1961, pp. 20, 36.

APPENDIX 3

Specimen Letter Report

BRADY AND WOOD

CONSULTING ENGINEERS

Los Angeles, California 90063

March 18, 1964

Delta Tube Company
122 E. Mariposa Street
Altadena, California 91002

Atten: Dr. J. Hearn
Chief Engineer

Gentlemen:

As you instructed, we bought one cylinder of Coast Chemical
Co. neon and analyzed the gas. We understand that you con-
template using Coast neon in counter tubes.

Only 92 parts per million of impurities were detected:
Nitrogen 45 ppm, Helium 25 ppm, Hydrogen 4 ppm, Oxygen 4
ppm, Hydrocarbons 12 ppm, and Moisture 2 ppm.

From the results of our tests, Coast Chemical Co. neon appears to be a high-purity reagent gas. This neon has 30
ppm less impurities than the gas you used last year.

We believe that you will be safe in using Coast Chemical
Co. neon in your long-life counter tubes. However, we ad-
vise you to spot-check this gas at regular intervals.

Thank you for this opportunity to serve you.

Sincerely,

BRADY AND WOOD

Scott L. Brady

SLB:dc

Scott L. Brady
President

cc: Analytical Lab

APPENDIX 4

Specimen Professional Report

DYNAMIC ENVIRONMENTS OF
THE S-IV AND S-IVB SATURN VEHICLES

BY
R.W. MUSTAIN
ACOUSTICS AND STRUCTURAL DYNAMICS SECTION
DOUGLAS AIRCRAFT COMPANY, INC.
MISSILE & SPACE SYSTEMS DIVISION
SPACE SYSTEMS CENTER
5301 BOLSA AVENUE
HUNTINGTON BEACH, CALIFORNIA

PRESENTED TO
THE 33RD SYMPOSIUM ON SHOCK, VIBRATION AND
ASSOCIATED ENVIRONMENTS, OFFICE OF THE
SECRETARY OF DEFENSE, WASHINGTON, D.C.
DECEMBER 5, 1963

DOUGLAS MISSILE & SPACE SYSTEMS DIVISION

ABSTRACT

The vibration and acoustic environments of the S-IV and S-IVB Stages of the
Saturn vehicle are summarized. A brief review of techniques used to predict
the dynamic environments of the S-IV and S-IVB vehicles is presented. This
review includes discussions on the prediction of rocket exhaust noise, boundary
layer noise, sinusoidal vibrations, and random vibrations for the S-IV and
S-IVB vehicles. In addition, sine-random vibration conversions are given.

Various prediction techniques are examined and compared. Predictions of S-IV
and S-IVB rocket exhaust noise are compared with field measurements. Different
methods of acoustic/vibration correlativity are utilized to provide environmental vibration levels for the S-IV and S-IVB vehicles. A curve of classical
vibration response to acoustic loading is given for use in the correlation of
acoustic levels with structural vibration levels. The prediction of both
sinusoidal and random vibrations is presented in considerable detail to provide illustrative examples. Typical tables of computations are included.

INTRODUCTION

A primary design consideration for the Saturn S-IV and S-IVB Stages is the effect of acoustical and vibrational excitations on the vehicle structure and on delicate airborne equipment. The importance of this consideration is enhanced by noting the severe dynamic environments which are produced by the high-thrust rocket systems of the Saturn Vehicle. In addition, attention must be given to the possible damaging effects of aerodynamic noise which results from turbulence in the boundary layer; this noise approaches its highest level during the maximum Q (dynamic pressure) phase of the flight mission. In view of the high-thrust rocket systems and the boundary layer noise excitations, there exists a fundamental requirement for an adequate definition of the dynamic environments of the S-IV and S-IVB Stages of the Saturn Vehicle. The definition of these environments is continually being up-dated; therefore, this paper presents only an interim report. The definition of the S-IV and S-IVB dynamic environments is being modified and improved progressively by field measurements and more refined prediction studies.

The acoustic and vibrational environments of the S-IV and S-IVB Stages of the Saturn Vehicle are discussed in this paper. Predictions and measurements of these dynamic environments are presented. Predicted acoustic time histories are given for the early phases of the S-IV and S-IVB missions. These time histories are compared with acoustic measurements from two flights of the Saturn I Vehicle. Prediction techniques for rocket exhaust noise and boundary layer noise are discussed briefly. Predictions of acoustic spectra for six S-IV engines (RL-10), without diffuser attenuation, are given. Measurements of acoustic levels during firings of the S-IVB engine are presented and compared with predicted levels.

Different methods of acoustic/vibration correlativity are utilized to provide environmental vibration levels for both the S-IV and S-IVB Stages. Various correlation techniques are compared and evaluated. A curve of classical vibration response to acoustic loading is given for use in the correlation of acoustic levels with structural vibration levels. Acoustic/vibration correlation methods are used to determine both sine and random vibration environments. Also, sine-random vibration conversions are used to establish random vibration levels for the S-IVB Stage.

1

SATURN CONFIGURATIONS

The S-IV, powered by six RL-10 engines, is the second stage of the
Saturn I; and the S-IVB, powered by one J-2 engine, is (1) the second stage
of the Saturn IB and (2) the third stage of the Saturn V (See Figure 1).
The primary mission of the Saturn I configuration is unmanned orbital flights
around the earth. The Saturn IB configuration has as its primary mission
the support of the basic Apollo mission by early testing of Apollo spacecraft
modules in earth orbital environments. The Saturn V is a three-stage vehicle
whose primary mission is lunar manned operations.

THE ACOUSTIC ENVIRONMENTS

The structure and the equipment on the S-IV and S-IVB Stages will be
exposed to acoustic forcing functions that are variant with time and the
mission profile. The following list of forcing functions presents some of
the acoustic sources that must be considered during the Saturn program
(reference 1):

1. Rocket engine noise.
2. Ancillary equipment.
3. Laminar boundary layer noise.
4. Turbulent boundary layer fluctuations.
5. Turbulent wakes (protuberated).
6. Base pressure fluctuations.
7. Cavity resonances.
8. Secondary acoustic sources.

Usually, the sound field of the rocket engine is the most important
source of vibration, and the boundary layer noise ranks second in source
severity; however, preliminary data show that the boundary layer noise on
the S-IV and S-IVB Stages is equal to or greater than the rocket engine
noise at some locations. This condition is being investigated; additional
measurements will be made during Saturn flights. During the launch phase
of the Saturn Vehicle, the tremendous noise generated by the rocket engines
is transmitted through the atmosphere and reflected by the ground plane
around the space vehicle. Since the rocket noise is essentially random and
"white" in nature, it creates resonant responses of skin panels and structures. The magnitude of this excitation depends upon the frequency spectrum,
the amplitude, the space correlation of the noise, and the mechanical impedance of the structure. The resulting vibrational energy is transferred

2

throughout the vehicle to substructure and equipment. Some of the panels act as secondary noise sources and radiate acoustic energy into the vehicle's compartments. In turn, some of these bays become semi-reverberant chambers to maintain fairly high acoustic levels. Rocket engine noise, reflected from the ground plane, dominates the Saturn environment for the first few seconds of flight until the Saturn Vehicle rises a distance equivalent to approximately 50 exit nozzle diameters. After the Saturn Vehicle leaves the launch pad, it begins to gain velocity; and then the effect of vehicle motion becomes apparent until, on approaching Mach one, the rocket noise does not propagate to the vehicle. As the Saturn Vehicle moves with increased velocity through the atmosphere, boundary layer noise becomes the dominant forcing function. Originally, the boundary layer noise is extremely low and is masked during the launch phase by the intense rocket engine noise, and is not propagated in any degree until the sonic speed range is reached. The boundary layer noise is a function of dynamic pressure and other related aerodynamic parameters such as the vehicle's attitude and configuration; the noise reaches its highest level during the maximum Q phase of the flight mission.

Figure 2 summarizes the acoustic environment of the S-IV and S-IVB Stages during the first 160 seconds of the flight mission. This chronological history of the major acoustic sources depicts (1) the sound pressure levels predicted for the S-IV and S-IVB Stages and (2) the sound pressure levels measured during Saturn I flights SA-3 and SA-4. The launch phase, the diminution immediately after launch, the increase in level to the maximum dynamic pressure, and the final decline to negligible noise levels are included in this summation. This set of curves shows that the boundary layer noise is equal to or greater than the rocket engine noise during the flight mission. These boundary layer noise levels are indicative of local flow conditions with large protuberances, and may be much less (approximately 14 db) on cleaner areas of the S-IV and S-IVB Stages where undisturbed boundary layer flow occurs. Four individual time history curves are displayed in Figure 2:

1. The predicted S-IV acoustic time history.
2. The predicted S-IVB acoustic time history.
3. Acoustic measurements obtained during the Saturn SA-3 flight internally on the SI Stage.
4. Acoustic measurements obtained during the Saturn SA-4 flight externally on the S-IV aft interstage.

3

SATURN CONFIGURATIONS

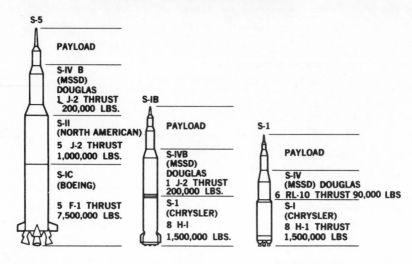

FIGURE 1

S-IV AND S-IVB ACOUSTIC TIME HISTORIES

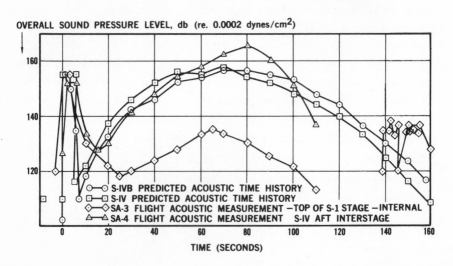

FIGURE 2

All of these curves show a reasonable likeness during the launch phase.
With the logical exception of the SA-3 data, the curves also show good
agreement during the maximum Q phase of the mission. That is, the SA-3
microphone was located on the lower SI Stage, was an internal measurement,
and consequently, the SA-3 data should not correlate well with the other data
during the maximum Q phase. Since the microphone on the SI Stage is the
closest acoustic measurement to the S-IV Stage, the SA-3 data are presented
only for general interest. The microphone on the fourth Saturn flight (SA-4)
was mounted flush with the skin of the S-IV aft interstage in a disturbed
flow region. Incidentally, the S-IV Stages on the SA-3 and SA-4 flights were
dummy stages. The highest boundary layer noise levels on Figure 2 are those
measured during the SA-4 flight. As a first approximation, these fluctuations
are assumed proportional to the freestream pressure:

$$OAFPL \text{ or } OASPL \cong 20 \log Q + K \quad db \tag{1}$$

where OAFPL is the level of the overall pressure fluctuations at the surface,
Q is the freestream dynamic pressure in lbs/sq.ft., and K is a factor which
varies with aerodynamic flow parameters. K is a function of the vehicle's
altitude, attitude, velocity, and configuration. The value of K will be
approximately 86 for an aerodynamically clean configuration with a zero angle
of attack. As drag increases, the value of K increases. Recent wind tunnel
tests performed at Douglas indicate that space vehicles, such as the Saturn,
with large protuberances, have related K factors as great as 110. A K value
of 100 was used to determine the S-IV and S-IVB predictions on Figure 2.
The protuberances are external vehicle items such as wiring ducts, fuel ducts,
ullage rockets, and the like.

Predictions of rocket engine noise from six RL-10 engines, without
diffusers, are shown in the three-dimensional display of Figure 3. The
sound pressure levels are given as a function of octave bands and location
forward of the engine nozzles. These levels are extremely conservative
since the S-IV Stage is static (or acceptance) fired with 27 foot diffusers
which exhaust against a deflector plate; therefore, these levels should be
lowered considerably for S-IV static firings. Two different prediction
methods, described in Reference 2, were used to calculate the noise from
the RL-10 engine. The 15,000 pound thrust engine produces a sound power
level of approximately 181 db overall (re 10^{-13} watts). The value of 181

db was found by using an empirical equation which was based on data from
rockets in the 1,000 to 130,000 pounds thrust range (Reference 3):

$$OAPWL = 78 + 13.5 \ \log_{10} W_m \tag{2}$$

where W_m = mechanical power of jetstream in watts,

$W_m = 0.676 \ tV = -.676 \ (t^2 g)/w,$

with $V = (tg)/w$ = gas velocity at nozzle exit in fps,

t = thrust in pounds,

g = acceleration due to gravity = 32.2 ft/sec^2,

w = weight flow in lb/sec

then

$$PWL = 78 + 13.5 \ \log \ 0.676 \ \frac{t^2 g}{w}$$

The empirical relationship of equation (2) remains a fairly reliable
prediction of the total acoustical power of conventionally fueled rockets
at sea-level operations (Reference 4).

Acoustic data obtained during test stand firings of the S-IVB engine,
the J-2, at Rocketdyne are summarized in Figure 4. The average sound pressure
levels from four test firings are plotted as a function of octave bands and
distance forward of the nozzle exit plane. Acoustic data, from Figure 4, for
the aft skirt are replotted in Figure 5 and compared with acoustic levels
which were determined by four different prediction methods:

1. WADC TR 58-343 (Reference 5).
2. WADC TR 57-354 (Reference 3).
3. Modified WADC TR 58-343 (Reference 6).
4. Scaled Thor data.

The highest levels on Figure 5 are displayed by the measured J-2 data,
especially in the second through fifth octave bands. The scaled Thor data
and the modified WADC data show a reasonable agreement with the measured
data at the higher frequencies. Following are the original measured data
on the Thor booster:

Octave Band	Sound Pressure Level
	db
1	141
2	144
3	146
4	147
5	146
6	145
7	144
8	143
overall	154

6

PREDICTED ACOUSTIC SPECTRA
6 RL-10 ENGINES WITHOUT DIFFUSER ATTENUATION

M-14469

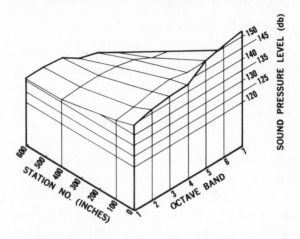

FIGURE 3

MEASURED S-IVB ENGINE
ACOUSTIC SPECTRA

M-14468

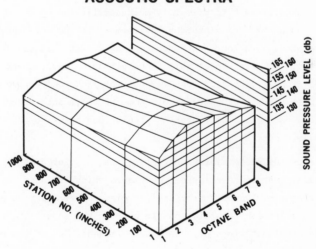

FIGURE 4

7

Using equation (2), the sound power levels were found to be 199 db re 10^{-13} watt for the Thor and 198 db re 10^{-13} watt for the J-2 engine at sea level. Then, the sound power level differential of one db was subtracted from the original Thor data. These lower levels are plotted on Figure 5 as the scaled Thor data.

S-IV VIBRATION PREDICTIONS AND MEASUREMENTS

Saturn rocket engine and boundary layer noise has, in general, a random distribution with broad spectra. As these acoustic excitations impinge on the S-IV Stage they induce random vibrations (with variant bandwidths) on the vehicle structure. This condition of randomness varies throughout the vehicle as the spectra are influenced by structural filters that create dominant peaks at response frequencies. Also, the random vibrations are assumed to have instantaneous accelerations (in any frequency band) that exhibit normal or Gaussian distributions. Perhaps, the most severe vibration environment occurs during the maximum Q phase of flight for a relatively short period of time. Lower vibration levels occur on the S-IV Stage during the acceptance (static) firings which are conducted on each S-IV Stage at the Sacramento, California facility of the Douglas Aircraft Company, Inc. The vibration levels during the S-IV acceptance firings are greatly reduced by the use of 27 foot diffusers which attenuate the acoustic excitations from the RL-10 engines. In addition, the S-IV Stage is supported by isolators during the acceptance firings to minimize the dynamic feedback from the test stand. Hence, the vibration environment of the S-IV Stage during the acceptance firings is primarily mechanically induced. Furthermore, it is highly probable that the vibration environment of the acceptance firings closely simulates the vibration environment during flight when the RL-10 engines are firing. In order to establish the vibration environment of the S-IV acceptance firings, vibration measurements were recorded during static firings of the S-IV-5 Stage at Sacramento. Some of these data are presented in this report and compared with vibration predictions based on the conservative acoustic levels of Figure 3.

Prior to discussing these vibration comparisons, a brief description is given of acoustic/vibration correlation techniques which are used in this paper to predict some of the S-IV vibration levels. Several investigators have attempted to establish the relationship between the acoustic forcing function and the resultant vibratory response. This has led to the establishment of vibration prediction techniques which are founded on acoustic/

8

**S-IVB
STATIC FIRING
ACOUSTIC
SPECTRA
AT AFT SKIRT**

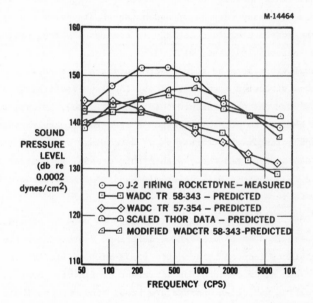

FIGURE 5

vibration correlativity. These prediction methods have used empirical information as their basis. Much remains to be desired on the accuracy of these various methods. The fault lies in the fact that these prediction methods are based on general data; consequently, these methods may not provide optimum predictions for specific cases.

Another drawback of most prediction techniques is the failure to account for structural resonances caused by structural filters. To explain further, predictions of random vibrations should display dominant peaks at response frequencies. However, most predictions show broad spectra which are in general agreement with typical vibration test specifications. This leads to conservative vibration test levels which may or may not be justified: This depends on the structural configuration. Relatively soft structures with many response frequencies should be tested to conservative specifications with broad spectra. In contrast, strong primary structure with a high natural frequency will have a dominant response peak. Then, the environmental vibrations on such a structure are best represented or estimated by a peaked vibration spectrum. Thus, ideal predictions should be based on actual knowledge of the structure being investigated. First, analytical techniques can be used to determine response spectra of structures. Secondly, response frequencies of structures can be determined by actual measurements. Finally, it can be expected that, within this decade, mechanical admittance or impedance measurements will be widely used to define structural response spectra and to determine transfer functions.

One of the popular empirical methods used to predict vibration levels is described in Reference 7. Reference 7 provides curves for predicting vibrations induced by acoustic excitations. Predictions using Reference 7 data can be determined for different confidence levels. However, these resulting vibration spectra are broad band such as those found in typical test specifications. Two additional curves for predicting acoustically induced vibrations are given in Figures 6 and 7. The correlation data of Figure 6 are based on Minuteman, Jupiter, Titan, and Skybolt measurements collected by E. F. Winter (Reference 8). The acoustic/vibration correlativity of Figure 7 was compiled by the author of this paper. The data in Figure 7 are representative of rigid primary structure with a dominant and high (say approximately 700 to 1200 cps) response frequency. These data tend to follow a classical transmissibility curve.

10

STRUCTURAL RESPONSE TO ACOUSTIC LOADING

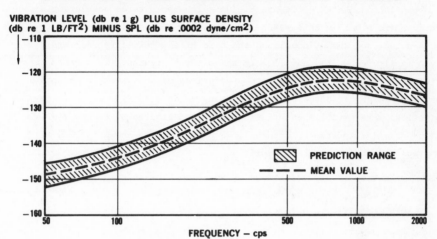

VIBRATION LEVEL (db re 1 g) PLUS SURFACE DENSITY
(db re 1 LB/FT^2) MINUS SPL (db re .0002 dyne/cm^2)

PREDICTION RANGE
— — — MEAN VALUE

FREQUENCY — cps

FIGURE 6

CLASSICAL RESPONSE TO ACOUSTIC LOADING

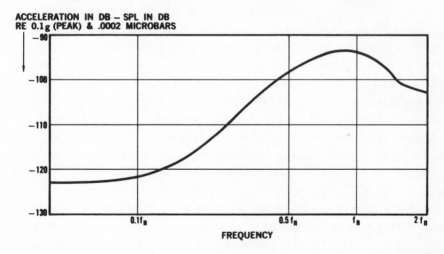

ACCELERATION IN DB — SPL IN DB
RE 0.1 g (PEAK) & .0002 MICROBARS

FREQUENCY

FIGURE 7

A large quantity of useful vibration data was obtained during two acceptance firings of the S-IV-5 Stage. The presentation of all the vibration data from the S-IV-5 firings is beyond the scope of this paper. The accelerometer locations during the S-IV-5 acceptance firings at Sacramento are shown in the sketch of Figure 8. Data from only three accelerometer locations are given in this report. Acceptance firing vibrations at the gimbal point, the thrust cone, and the base of the telemetry rack are displayed in Figures 9, 10, and 11. In these three figures, the acceptance firing vibrations are compared with predictions of acoustically induced vibrations which are based on the RL-10 engine data of Figure 3. These predictions were established by using data from Figures 3, 6, and 7 of this paper and data from Reference 7. Four curves are shown in each of the graphs of figures 9, 10, and 11:

1. Vibration levels determined by the method of reference 7 (95% confidence, Smith and Mahaffey).

2. Vibration levels determined by using the data in Figure 6 of this paper.

3. Vibration levels determined by using the data on the classical curve of Figure 7.

4. Measured vibration levels from the acceptance firings of the S-IV-5 Stage at Sacramento, California.

Three tables showing typical data for each of the prediction methods are given in addendum A which accompanies this paper.

The predicted vibration levels in Figures 9, 10, and 11 are based on the acoustic levels shown in Figure 3; consequently, these predicted vibrations are much greater than the actual acoustically induced vibrations on the S-IV acceptance firings. Since the actual S-IV acceptance firings are made with diffusers, the static firing acoustic levels are much lower than the levels of Figure 3. In turn, the acoustically induced vibrations during the static firings are much less than the predictions in Figures 9, 10, and 11. Whereas the S-IV acceptance firings are made with diffusers which attenuate most of the sound, the vibrations on the S-IV Stage during the acceptance firings are almost entirely mechanically induced. A study of Figures 9, 10, and 11 shows that the mechanically induced vibrations during the acceptance firings are approximately equal to predicted acoustically induced vibrations from six unattenuated RL-10 engines. Originally, these figures were prepared to show the differential between mechanically induced

12

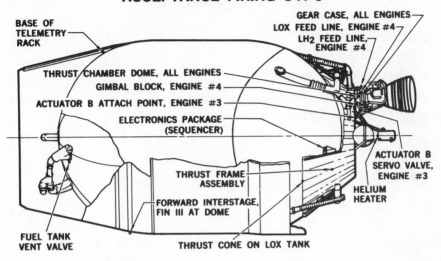

ACCELEROMETER LOCATIONS
ACCEPTANCE FIRING S-IV-5

M-14457

BASE OF TELEMETRY RACK

GEAR CASE, ALL ENGINES
LOX FEED LINE, ENGINE #4
LH2 FEED LINE, ENGINE #4

THRUST CHAMBER DOME, ALL ENGINES
GIMBAL BLOCK, ENGINE #4
ACTUATOR B ATTACH POINT, ENGINE #3
ELECTRONICS PACKAGE (SEQUENCER)

ACTUATOR B SERVO VALVE, ENGINE #3

THRUST FRAME ASSEMBLY

HELIUM HEATER

FORWARD INTERSTAGE, FIN III AT DOME

FUEL TANK VENT VALVE

THRUST CONE ON LOX TANK

FIGURE 8

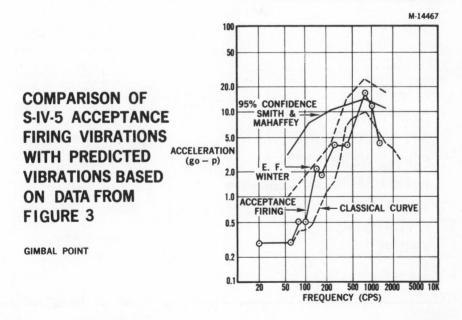

COMPARISON OF S-IV-5 ACCEPTANCE FIRING VIBRATIONS WITH PREDICTED VIBRATIONS BASED ON DATA FROM FIGURE 3

GIMBAL POINT

M-14467

95% CONFIDENCE SMITH & MAHAFFEY

E. F. WINTER

ACCELERATION (go – p)

ACCEPTANCE FIRING

CLASSICAL CURVE

FREQUENCY (CPS)

FIGURE 9

COMPARISON OF S-IV-5 ACCEPTANCE FIRING VIBRATIONS WITH PREDICTED VIBRATIONS BASED ON DATA FROM FIGURE 3

THRUST CONE

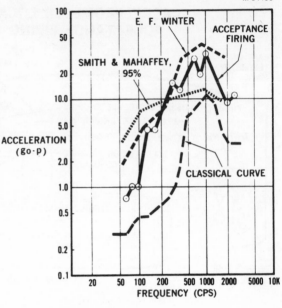

FIGURE 10

COMPARISON OF S-IV-5 ACCEPTANCE FIRING VIBRATIONS WITH PREDICTED VIBRATIONS BASED ON DATA FROM FIGURE 3

BASE OF T/M

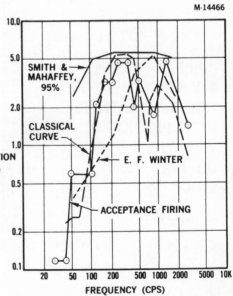

FIGURE 11

vibrations (acceptance firing data) and acoustically induced vibrations (the predicted vibrations). However, the predicted and the measured vibrations show an unexpected agreement which indicates that the S-IV engine/vehicle transfer function results in relatively high mechanically induced vibrations. This transfer function includes the effects of multiple engine dynamics on the S-IV structure. Also, some of the mechanically induced vibrations may be attributed to accessories on the six RL-10 engines. This subject of mechanically and acoustically induced vibration on the S-IV Stage is an interesting one that requires further analysis. This relationship will be better defined as microphone measurements and additional vibration measurements become available from future S-IV acceptance firings.

The next four figures, 12 through 15, show predictions of the acoustically induced vibrations during launch and flight of the S-IV Stage (Reference 9). In each figure, an envelope has been drawn over the 95% confidence level (Smith and Mahaffey) to provide a conservative test level. This test level is applied as a one minute per octave sinusoidal logarithmic sweep. With this sweep rate, a test specimen is exposed to each resonance for approximately 35 seconds (Reference 9). Predicted vibrations on the extreme aft S-IV interstage are plotted on Figure 12. The vibration environment of Figure 12 is based on wind tunnel data for the maximum Q phase and on SI acoustic data for the lift-off phase. Both the maximum Q and the lift-off predictions of Figure 12 were determined by using the data from Reference 7. The vibration environments of the aft interstage (Figure 13), the thrust structure (Figure 14), and the forward interstage (Figure 15), are based on acoustic data which were obtained from the Saturn SA-4 flight and from SI Stage static firings. Figures 13, 14, and 15 display comparative vibration levels which were obtained by using the data of Figures 6 and 7 of this paper and the data from Reference 7. Curves A, C, and D display a reasonable agreement. The best agreement is noted near the response frequency of the structure where curves C and D peak. The poorest correlation can be found at the lower frequencies where the broad spectrum of curve A exists. Curve A is typical of specifications which provide overly conservative test levels. The reason for the difference in the low frequency levels is probably due to the fact that curve A is an envelope of vibration levels of light components attached to light flexible structure. Curves B, C, and D are considered to envelop vibration levels measured on heavy primary structure.

PREDICTION OF ACOUSTICALLY AND PRESSURE FLUCTUATION INDUCED VIBRATION–EXTREME AFT OF S-I/S-IV INTERSTAGE

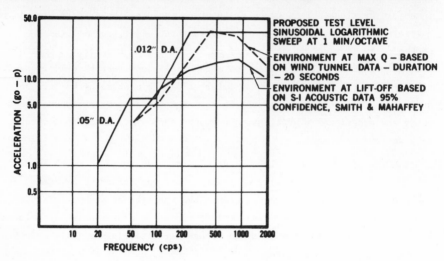

FIGURE 12

PREDICTIONS OF ACOUSTICALLY INDUCED VIBRATION–AFT INTERSTAGE OF S-IV

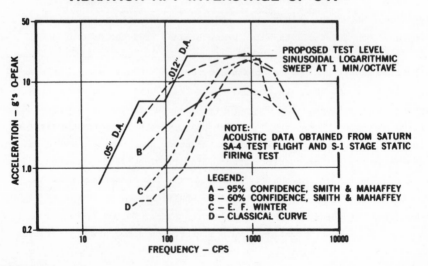

FIGURE 13

PREDICTIONS OF ACOUSTICALLY INDUCED VIBRATION-THRUST STRUCTURE OF S-IV

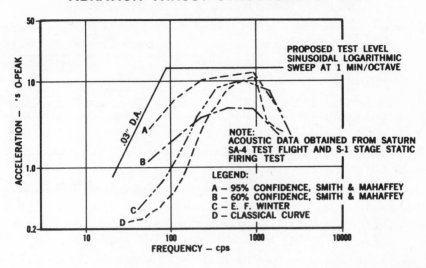

FIGURE 14

PREDICTIONS OF ACOUSTICALLY INDUCED VIBRATION-FORWARD INTERSTAGE OF S-IV

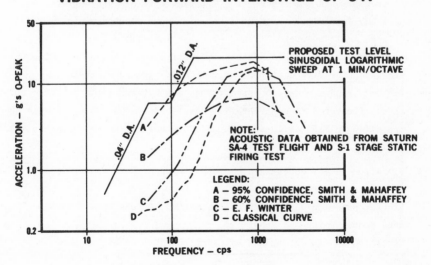

FIGURE 15

S-IVB VIBRATION PREDICTIONS

An exploded view of the Saturn S-IVB Stage is presented in Figure 16. Similar to the S-IV dynamic environment, the S-IVB vibration environment has, in general, a random distribution with broad spectra. The bandwidth of these random vibrations varies throughout the vehicle as the spectra are influenced by structural filters that create dominant peaks at response frequencies. Furthermore, the instantaneous accelerations are assumed to have normal distributions or slight modifications of the normal distribution, and the corresponding peaks are assumed to be distributed according to the Rayleigh law. The S-IVB vibrations will be significant during the lift-off phase, the maximum Q phase, and the J-2 engine firing phase. The lift-off vibrations and the maximum Q vibrations of the S-IVB Stage will be similar in severity to the S-IV lift-off and maximum Q vibrations. The vibrations during the S-IVB acceptance firings will be greater than the vibrations during the S-IV acceptance firings because of the more severe acoustical environment. Likewise, the mechanically induced vibrations from the J-2 engine during S-IVB flight will be greater than the flight vibrations from the RL-10 engines on the S-IV Stage because of the increased engine size and thrust. Since the vibrations during the S-IVB acceptance firings will rank high in importance, predictions have been made of acoustically induced vibrations on the S-IVB static firings.

These predictions were established by using data from Figures 4, 6, 7, and 17 of this paper and data from Reference 7. Figure 17 of this paper was originally presented in Reference 10. This figure is useful in proposal stages and early design stages where little is known about a vehicle. To use this figure, only an overall sound pressure level is required; this technique provides a reasonable "ball-park" estimation. Random vibration spectra are given for five different overall sound pressure levels in Figure 17. Only random vibration predictions are given for the S-IVB acceptance firings. Predicted random vibration levels for the S-IVB acceptance firings are given in Figures 18 and 19. Five curves are shown in each of the graphs of Figures 18 and 19:

1. Vibration levels determined by the methods of Reference 7 (95% confidence, Smith and Mahaffey).
2. Vibration levels determined by the method of Reference 7 (60% confidence, Smith and Mahaffey).
3. Vibration levels determined by using the data in Figure 6 of this paper.

18

SATURN S-IVB STAGE EXPLODED VIEW

M-14463

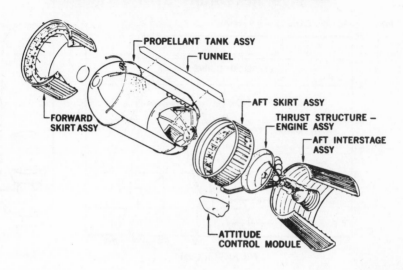

PROPELLANT TANK ASSY

TUNNEL

FORWARD
SKIRT ASSY

AFT SKIRT ASSY

THRUST STRUCTURE –
ENGINE ASSY

AFT INTERSTAGE
ASSY

ATTITUDE
CONTROL MODULE

FIGURE 16

TEST REQUIRE – MENT ENVELOPES FOR VARIOUS ACOUSTIC NOISE LEVELS

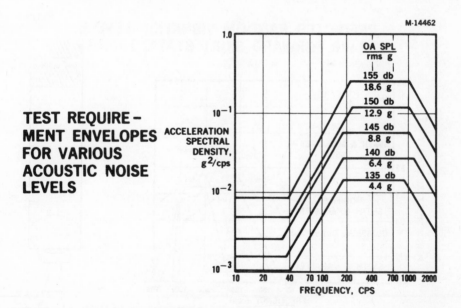

FIGURE 17

PREDICTED RANDOM VIBRATION LEVELS
S-IVB AFT SKIRT STATIC FIRING

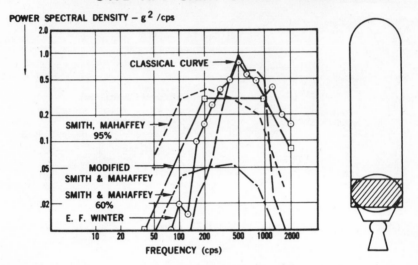

POWER SPECTRAL DENSITY – g^2/cps

CLASSICAL CURVE

SMITH, MAHAFFEY 95%

MODIFIED SMITH & MAHAFFEY

SMITH & MAHAFFEY 60%

E. F. WINTER

FREQUENCY (cps)

FIGURE 18

PREDICTED RANDOM VIBRATION LEVELS
S-IVB FORWARD SKIRT STATIC FIRING

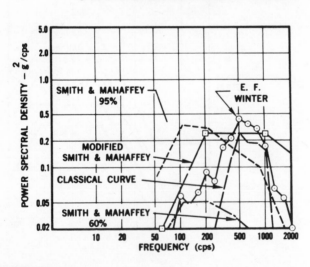

POWER SPECTRAL DENSITY – g^2/cps

SMITH & MAHAFFEY 95%

E. F. WINTER

MODIFIED SMITH & MAHAFFEY

CLASSICAL CURVE

SMITH & MAHAFFEY 60%

FREQUENCY (cps)

FIGURE 19

4. Vibration levels determined by using the data on the classical curve of Figure 7.

5. Vibration levels determined by using the data of Figure 17.

Three tables showing typical data on three of the prediction methods are given in addendum B of this paper. For additional information on predicting random vibration levels from Figure 7 and on sine-random conversions, the reader is referred to Reference 1. All of the curves labeled "Smith and Mahaffey" and "E. F. Winter" were determined by first finding sinusoidal vibration levels and then converting to random vibration levels by using the following equation from Reference 1:

$$G = \frac{0.174\ (Ap)^2}{f} \qquad (3)$$

where G = mean squared acceleration density or power spectral density in g^2/cps, A_p is the peak applied sinusoidal vibration, and f is the frequency of resonance.

A reasonable correlation is noticed on Figures 18 and 19. In Figure 18, the classical curve and the E. F. Winter curve display an excellent agreement. Also, the Smith and Mahaffey 95% curve and the Modified Smith and Mahaffey curve are in good agreement. The main difference is in the frequency range; this difference is a natural result of the two different techniques. The predicted random vibration levels of the S-IVB forward skirt (Figure 19) are less than the predicted vibration levels on the aft skirt. In Figure 19, all of the curves, except the Smith and Mahaffey 60% curve, compare very well. The predictions in Figures 18 and 19 provide useful vibration levels which establish a vibration gradient for the S-IVB Stage, and which are currently being used to determine S-IVB vibration test levels.

CONCLUSION

This paper has presented a brief review of the acoustic and vibration environments of the S-IV and S-IVB Stages of the Saturn Vehicle. Only a fragment of the available data was covered in this interim paper. Predictions and measurements of the acoustic and vibration environments were given. Predicted acoustic time histories for the early phases of the S-IV and S-IVB missions were presented. These acoustic predictions were compared with Saturn I flight data. Predictions of acoustic spectra for six S-IV engines (RL-10), without diffuser attenuation, were given. This presentation included a summary of acoustic data from J-2 engine firings.

Environmental vibration levels for both the S-IV and S-IVB Stages were determined by using different methods of acoustic/vibration correlativity. Comparisons were made of the results obtained by the different correlation techniques. These methods were used to determine both sine and random vibration environments. Vibration data measured during the S-IV-5 acceptance firing were presented and discussed.

Much work remains to be done in the definition of the S-IV and S-IVB acoustical and vibrational environments. More vibration measurements will be acquired during static firings and flights of both the S-IV and S-IVB Stages. In addition, microphone measurements will be obtained. A continuous and necessary effort is underway to adequately define the acoustical and vibrational environments of the S-IV and S-IVB Stages.

ACKNOWLEDGEMENT

The writer is greatly indebted to K. E. Elliott, J. W. Lew, P. M. Lewis, J. C. McClymonds, T. D. Schoessow, P. F. Spas, and E. F. Winter of the Douglas Missile and Space Systems Division for their contributions to this paper.

REFERENCES

1. R. W. Mustain, "Prediction of Random Environments", 1963 SAE National Aeronautic and Space Engineering and Manufacturing Meeting, September 23-27 at the Ambassador, Los Angeles.

2. R. W. Mustain, "On the Prediction of Dynamic Environments", Bulletin No. 28 Shock, Vibration, and Associated Environments Part IV, Office of the Secretary of Defense, August 1960.

3. WADC Technical Report, 57-354, "Noise Radiation from Fourteen Types of Rockets in the 1000 to 130,000 Pounds Thrust Range", December 1957.

4. Northrop Report, NOR-60-26, "Structural Vibration in Space Vehicles", Phase I Report, "Investigation of Structural Vibration Sources and Characteristics".

5. WADC Technical Report 58-343, "Methods of Space Vehicle Noise Prediction", September 1960.

6. P. A. Franken and F. M. Wiener, "Estimation of Noise Levels at the Surface of a Rocket-Powered Vehicle", Bolt Beranek and Newman Inc., Los Angeles, California and Cambridge, Massachusetts.

7. P. T. Mahaffey and K. W. Smith, "A Method for Predicting Environmental Vibration Levels in Jet-Powered Vehicles", Bulletin No. 28 Shock, Vibration, and Associated Environments Part IV, Office of the Secretary of Defense, August 1960.

8. Personal communication from E. F. Winter, Douglas Missile and Space Systems Division, to R. W. Mustain.

9. J. C. McClymonds and J. W. Lew, "Proposed Deviation from MSFC Vibration Specification IN-P&VE-S-62-7", Douglas Missile & Space Systems Division, 4 September 1963.

10. H. Himelblau and A. G. Piersol, "Summary of Nortronics Modification of Mahaffey Smith Procedure", October 1963.

Acoustic/vibration correlativity

I. Vibration levels determined by the method of Reference 7 (Smith and Mahaffey). The basic data for the curve (95% confidence, Smith and Mahaffey) in Figure 9 are given in Table I. These curves have been drawn through points plotted at the geometric mean frequencies (GMF = $\sqrt{f_1 \times f_2}$) of the octave bands. Octave band widths were used in agreement with the method of Reference 7.

Table I

Octave Bands	GMF	SPL (db)	60% g's (o-peak)	95% g's (o-peak)
37.5 - 75	53	137.6	1.4	3.2
75 - 150	106	138.9	2.5	7.2
150 - 300	212	140.2	3.7	10.0
300 - 600	425	140.6	5.0	11.5
600 - 1200	850	139.0	5.2	13.3
1200 - 2400	1700	139.5	4.4	10.8

II. Vibration levels determined by using the data in Figure 6 of this paper. The calculations for the E. F. Winter curve in Figure 9 are given in Table II for the gimbal point of the S-IV Stage. This curve was determined by using the data in Figure 6 and the following basic relationship:

$$20 \log_{10} g_{rms} = SPL + TF - 20 \log_{10} W \text{ (in db re/g)}$$

where W = surface density in lb/ft^2

TF = transfer function (ordinate of Figure 6)

SPL = sound pressure level (db)

$20 \log g_{rms}$ is in db re 1 g

Table II

$$20 \log_{10} W = -0.72$$

1	2	3	4	5	6	7	8
Octave Band	GMF	SPL	TF	3+4	Col. 5-20 log W in db re 1g	g_{rms}	g (o-peak)
37.5 - 75	53	137.6	-148	-10.4	-9.7	.32	1.0
75 - 150	106	138.9	-143	-4.1	-3.4	.68	2.0
150 - 300	212	140.2	-138	2.2	2.9	1.40	4.2
300 - 600	425	140.6	-128	12.6	13.3	4.70	14.1
600 - 1200	850	139.0	-122	17.0	17.7	7.80	23.4
1200 - 2400	1700	139.5	-125	14.5	15.2	5.75	17.3

III. Vibration levels determined by using the data in the classical curve
of Figure 7. The calculations for the (classical) vibration levels in
Figure 9 are listed in Table III. These vibrations display a dominant peak
which is characteristic of rigid primary structure. In this case, a response frequency of approximately 800 cps was assumed. Since the correlation data in Figure 7 were obtained from actual 1/3 octave acoustic and
vibration measurements, they are applicable to 1/3 octave predictions.
The octave-band sound pressure levels listed in Tables I and II were con-
verted to 1/3 octave-band sound pressure levels by simply subtracting
5 db from the octave-band sound pressure levels. Table III used the
relationship:

$$20 \log_{10} (g_{peak}/g_{ref}) = SPL + TF \qquad (\text{in db re } 0.1g)$$

where SPL = sound pressure level in 1/3 octave bands (db)

TF = Transfer function (ordinate of Figure 7)

Table III

1	2	3	4	5	6
f 1/3 octave Band	TF	1/3 Octave SPL (db)	Column 2 + Column 3 in db	Ratio g peak 0.1 g equivalent to db of col. 4	Col. 5x0.1 in g's (o-peak)
40	-123	132.6	9.6	3.0	.3
50	-123	132.6	9.6	3.0	.3
63	-123	132.6	9.6	3.0	.3
80	-121	133.9	12.9	4.5	.45
100	-121	133.9	12.9	4.5	.45
125	-120	133.9	13.9	5.0	.5
160	-117	135.2	18.2	8.15	.815
200	-115	135.2	20.2	10.2	1.02
250	-112	135.2	23.2	14.5	1.45
315	-108	135.6	27.6	24.0	2.40
400	-99	135.6	36.6	67.5	6.75
500	-97	135.6	38.6	85.0	8.50
630	-95	134.0	39.0	89.0	8.90
800	-94	134.0	40.0	100.0	10.0
1000	-97	135.0	37.0	71.0	7.10
1250	-100	134.5	34.5	53.0	5.30
1600	-103	134.5	31.5	38.0	3.80
2000	-104	134.5	30.5	34.0	3.40
2500	-106	134.5	28.5	26.6	2.66

Random Vibration Predictions

I. Random vibration levels determined by the method of Reference 7
(Smith and Mahaffey) and the use of equation (3). The basic data for
the Smith and Mahaffey 95% curve in Figure 18 are given in Table IV.
These curves have been drawn through points which were plotted at the
geometric mean frequencies (GMF = $\sqrt{f_1 \times f_s}$) of the octave bands.
Octave band widths were used in agreement with the method of Reference 7.

Table IV

Octave Bands	GMF	SPL (db)	95% g's (o-p)	95% g^2/cps
37.5 - 75	53	143	4.4	.07
75 - 150	106	148	13.5	.30
150 - 300	212	152	21.8	.39
300 - 600	425	152	27.0	.30
600 - 1200	850	149	29.5	.20
1200 - 2400	1700	144	15.7	.03

II. Random vibration levels determined by using the data in Figure 6 and by using equation (3). The calculations for the E. F. Winter curve in Figure 18 are given in Table V. The data in Figure 6 and the following basic relationship are used:

$$20 \log_{10} g_{rms} = SPL + TF - 20 \log_{10} W \qquad \text{(in db re 1g)}$$

where W = surface density in lb/ft^2

TF = Transfer function (ordinate of Figure 6)

SPL = sound pressure level (db)

$W = 1 \ lb/ft^2$; $20 \log W = 0$

Table V

1	2	3	4	5	6	7	8	9	10
f CPS	SPL db	TF db	Col.2 +Col.3	Col.4- 20 log W	g_{rms}	g(o-p)	g^2	$.174g^2$	g^2/cps
40	138	-150	-12	-12	0.25	0.75	0.565	.098	.0025
50	138	-148	-10	-10	0.32	0.96	0.925	.161	.0032
63	138	-147	-9	-9	0.55	1.65	2.72	.473	.0075
80	143	-146	-3	-3	0.71	2.17	5.08	.885	.0111
100	143	-144	-1	-1	1.1	3.3	10.95	1.91	.0191
125	143	-142	1	1	1.1	3.3	10.95	1.91	.0153
160	149	-139	10	10	3.17	9.5	90.4	15.75	.0985
200	149	-136	13	13	4.47	13.3	177	30.8	.154
250	149	-133	16	16	6.32	19.0	361	62.7	.251
315	149	-130	19	19	8.80	26.4	700	122	.387
400	149	-128	21	21	11.2	33.6	1134	197.5	.494
500	149	-125	24	24	15.8	47.4	2260	395	.779
630	146	-122.5	23.5	23.5	14.95	44.8	2020	351	.557
800	146	-122	24	24	15.8	47.4	2260	395	.493
1000	146	-123	23	23	14.1	42.2	1790	312	.312
1250	139	-124	15	15	5.62	16.9	286	49.7	.397
1600	139	-126	13	13	4.47	13.3	177	30.8	.193
2000	139	-126	13	13	4.47	13.3	177	30.8	.154

III. Random vibration levels determined by using the data in the classical curve of Figure 7. The calculations for the classical curve of Figure 18 are listed in Table VI. These vibrations display a dominant peak which is characteristic of rigid primary structure. In this case, a response frequency of approximately 900 cps was assumed. Since the correlation data in Figure 7 were obtained from actual 1/3 octave acoustic and vibration measurements, they are applicable to 1/3 octave predictions. Table VI uses the relationship:

$$20 \log_{10} (g_{peak}/g_{ref}) = SPL + TF \qquad \text{(in db re 0.1g)}$$

where SPL = sound pressure level in 1/3 octave bands

TF = transfer function (ordinate of Figure 7)

Table VI

1	2	3	4	5	6	7	8	9
f 1/3 octave band	TF	SPL db	Spectrum Level Conversion	$20 \log g_{peak}$ 0.1 g	g_{peak} 0.1 g	g peak	g_{rms}	g^2/cps
40	-123	138	-9.6	5.4	1.86	.19	.06	.004
50	-122.5	138	-10.6	4.9	1.78	.18	.06	.004
63	-122	138	-11.6	4.4	1.66	.17	.06	.004
80	-122	143	-12.6	8.4	2.63	.26	.09	.008
100	-121.5	143	-13.6	7.9	2.51	.25	.08	.006
125	-120.5	143	-14.6	7.9	2.51	.25	.08	.006
160	-118.5	147	-15.6	12.9	4.5	.45	.15	.023
200	-116	147	-16.6	14.4	5.3	.53	.18	.033
250	-112	147	-17.6	17.4	7.4	.74	.25	.063
315	-106	147	-18.6	22.4	13.3	1.33	.44	.194
400	-101	147	-19.6	26.4	20.9	2.1	.70	.49
500	-97	147	-20.6	29.4	29.5	2.95	.98	.96
630	-95	144	-21.6	27.4	23.5	2.35	.78	.61
800	-94	144	-22.6	27.4	23.5	2.35	.78	.61
1000	-94	144	-23.6	26.4	20.9	2.1	.70	.49
1250	-101	139	-24.6	13.4	4.65	.465	.15	.023
1600	-103	139	-25.6	10.4	3.31	.33	.11	.012
2000	-105	139	-26.6	7.4	2.35	.23	.08	.006

APPENDIX 5

Specimen Laboratory Report

LABORATORY TEST REPORT

NUMBER: 1580

DATE: May 12, 1962

TECHNICIAN: H.L.W.

OBJECT

To determine if Type DQY-1, 1000-ohm, $\pm$ 1%, 1-watt carbon
film resistors remain in tolerance at high temperature.
These resistors must operate at 50°C maximum in the new
Model 20 Strain Gauge Test Set.

APPARATUS

One Biddle Model 603207 Portable Wheatstone Bridge (Laboratory Inventory No. A200).

One Composite Adjustable-Temperature Laboratory Test Oven
with 20 Switched Test Stations (Laboratory Inventory No.
B761).

PROCEDURE

(1) Twenty sample resistors were numbered and clipped into
place on the selector turret inside the oven. (2) Next,
the bridge was connected to the oven test terminals, the
oven closed, and the test setup checked initially by rotating the turret successively to each of its 20 test positions and testing the corresponding resistance with the
bridge. (3) Then, the thermostat was set for 50°C and the
oven was switched on. No tests were attempted until 30
minutes after the oven temperature had stabilized at 50
degrees, to insure complete heat soak of the resistors.
(4) Finally, each resistor was switched successively to
the bridge, by rotating the turret, and its resistance
measured. (5) The resistance values were recorded (see
data sheet under OBSERVATIONS), and the deviation (D)

values were calculated by means of the formulas:
+D% = 0.1(R-1000) when the measured resistance is higher
than the nominal resistance of 1000 ohms; -D% = 0.1(1000-R)
when the measured resistance R is lower than 1000 ohms.

OBSERVATIONS

RESISTOR NO.	RESISTANCE (Ohms, 50°C)	DEVIATION (%)
1	1002.4	+0.24
2	1007.7	+0.77
3.	997.3	-0.27
4	1006.2	+0.62
5	991.3	-0.87
6.	1009.1	+0.91
7	995.8	-0.42
8	1005.3	+0.53
9	994.0	-0.60
10	1006.8	+0.68
11	993.7	-0.63
12	992.7	-0.73
13	994.4	-0.56
14	1004.7	+0.47
15	1008.4	+0.84
16	1007.2	+0.72
17	991.1	-0.89
18	1006.5	+0.65
19	992.4	-0.76
20	993.1	-0.69

Components in the 20-resistor lot vary between 991.1 and
1009.1 ohms. This represents an error spread of +0.91%
to -0.89%. Average positive deviation is 0.643%; average
negative deviation is 0.648%.

CONCLUSION

At 50°C, all 20 resistors in the test sampling remain within
the manufacturer's ± 1% resistance tolerance.

APPENDIX 6

---◆---

Specimen Final Draft of a Professional Report

AIR FORCE MATERIALS LABORATORY
RESEARCH AND TECHNOLOGY DIVISION
AIR FORCE SYSTEMS COMMAND

CONTRACT AF 33(615)-1235
PROJECT 7381; TASK 738103

THE PURPOSE AND

FUNCTIONS OF

THE ELECTRONIC PROPERTIES

INFORMATION CENTER

-- H. Thayne Johnson, Head
   Electronic Properties
   Information Center
   Hughes Aircraft Company
   Culver City, California

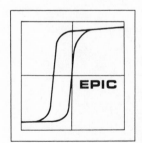 

HUGHES

HUGHES AIRCRAFT COMPANY
CULVER CITY, CALIFORNIA

FOREWORD

This report was prepared by Hughes Aircraft Company under Contract
AF 33(615)-1235 with the United States Air Force. It was initiated under
Project No. 1(8-7381), Task No. 738103. The work is administered under
the direction of the Air Force Materials Laboratories with Mr. R. F. Klinger
as Air Force Project Engineer.

Many persons have contributed to the development of the project
and therefore indirectly to this report. Presently, the most important
contributors are: J. W. Atwood, C. L. Blocher, D. L. Grigsby, D. H. Johnson,
T. J. Lyndon, J. T. Milek, and M. S. Neuberger.

ABSTRACT

An information retrieval system has been established for abstracting, indexing, and retrieving documents and data on the electrical
and electronic properties of materials. The indexing system for the
documents is a coordinate index, usable as both a manual and a machine
system of storage and retrieval. The data is synthesized from the literature and issued as data sheets, tables, and summary and special reports.
The documentation and compilation methods are described and examples are
given.

TABLE OF CONTENTS

v

INTRODUCTION

The number one problem in industry today - the problem which encompasses all research and development - is how to make available needed information from the myriads of publications that are daily being published. To the librarian or documentalist it is a problem of keeping from sinking into a morass of the very thing he deals in. To the engineer or scientist it is a problem of finding the facts he needs, of not needlessly duplicating research, or of cutting the lead time on an important project. Yet the tremendous explosion of research and development is complicating the entire informational picture.

Consider, for example, the following statistics:

World War II and the subsequent Cold War have spurred a phenomenal advance in science and technology. One pertinent example is in electronic computers.

The first large-scale computers were used during World War II for ballistic calculations; in the early 1950's they were introduced as commercial machines. By 1960, the total number of computers in the U.S. alone amounted to about 500 large-scale machines and some 3,000 medium or small units. Reasonable estimates forecast about 15,000 by 1965. It has been estimated that in the years 1950 to 1953 there was more computing than had been done by all mankind previously. By 1957 the figure doubled. It seems likely that some time in 1962 it had doubled again.

Such an exponential rise is not limited to aspects of data processing. The same type of growth pattern has been repeated again and again in the physical sciences, in nuclear physics, electronics and electronic devices, materials and their use, and in numerous other fields. Scientists and engineers have more than quadrupled in number since 1930 (from about 260,000 to over 1,200,000). It has been estimated that, of all the scientists and engineers who have ever lived, 90% of them are alive and actively working today. Funds earmarked for research and development have increased from $5 billion in 1953 to $14 billion in 1961, and are estimated at $30 billion per year by 1970.

In 1948, the remarkable invention of the transistor opened the whole world of solid state physics and began leading us in spectacular directions. The ability to understand and modify electron action in solids brought with it the desire to experiment with ultra pure materials. Since then, developments have evolved so fast that it sometimes seems impossible to say which came first, the theory or the new material. And now in addition we find ourselves concerned with such exotic activities as cryogenics, radiation, high temperatures, microminiaturization, and others, all at a level of research unheard of just a few short years ago.

Out of all this we have a new concern for informational problems. The unwarranted expenditure of large sums, the wasting of precious man-hours, the duplication of effort, the desire to cut the lead time of a project, all present a problem. There are three facets to this problem: (1) The basic need for securing information, (2) the mass of material from which this information must come, and (3) the need for rapid delivery. To meet the challenge, we find ourselves dealing with a whole new field and with a new breed of information scientist-engineer - part chemist, part physicist, part metallurgist, part ceramicist - who can show the technical abilities of others in these fields and yet demonstrate enough mixture of librarian to sympathize with and handle the informational problems of the literature. To this field and to these people are en-trusted the answers to the question: How can we adequately utilize the experimental data pouring in so fast from our laboratories?

The Air Force Materials Information Center of the Air Force Materials Laboratories has one answer - financially supporting the es-tablishment and maintenance of technical information analysis centers whose responsibility is to accumulate and index the literature and to synthesize the data in a highly specialized field of materials. One of these programs is described in this report - the Electronic Properties Information Center located at Hughes Aircraft Company, Culver City, California.

The Electronic Properties Information Center

Although unique in its systematic and organized approach to the
data contained in the literature, the Electronic Properties Information
Center (EPIC) is also somewhat representative in the philosophies and
concepts of the specialized information center. The program of EPIC is
to collect, index, and abstract the literature on the electrical and
electronic properties of materials, and to evaluate and compile the experimental data from this literature. It is estimated that hundreds of
thousands of items will be examined for inclusion, and that out of these
about 40,000 items, extending back to 1940, will be included. In addition
to these 40,000 items, it is estimated that the growth rate of literature
in this specialized field is about 3000 per year. These will constitute
a highly selective technical information center, complete with a specialized, modified coordinate index and a systematic approach to synthesizing,
evaluating, and compiling the experimental data.

EPIC was organized in June 1961, to cover nine major categories
of materials: semiconductors, insulators, ferroelectric dielectrics,
metals, ferrites, ferromagnetics, electroluminescent materials, thermionic
emitters, and superconductors. It was to be of service to materials
engineers and researchers by:

1. Collecting, indexing, and abstracting all literature
    containing experimental data on the electrical and elec-
    tronic properties of materials.

2. Answering technical questions through use of that literature.

3. Compiling bibliographies and making literature searches.

4. Writing commentaries and other special reports.

5. Synthesizing and, in an organized manner, evaluating and
    compiling the data from that literature.

The Indexing Vocabulary

A prime concern of the program has been studies to establish
categories, subcategories and properties to be covered. Considerable
difficulty was experienced in delineating those to be included as indexing
terms to the literature and data. Just in the insulator category, over
800 names of materials, including many trade names, were considered for
use. Semiconductor materials presented an array of elements, compounds,
mixtures, and systems that made it extremely difficult to correctly name

and categorize the material at hand. For example, a material composed of the elements aluminum, copper, and sulfur might be a true compound, an aluminum copper sulfide, a mixture of aluminum sulfide and copper sulfide, or a three-element system whose phase diagram will indicate certain areas within which specific compounds exist. Decisions had to be made as to the order of various elements in a name. For example, would a compound of tin and antimony appear as antimony stannide (alphabetically) or as tin antimonide (by group in the periodic table)? The former method was arbitrarily chosen.

By keeping the philosophy as simple as possible, other basic procedures were also set. It was determined that the generic chemical name (polyethylene terephthalate plastics) would always be used in the prime indexing vocabulary, and that the "see-reference" would always be made from the trade name (Mylar). By the establishment of simple rules such as these, it has become possible to explain the use of the index in a simple manner, without confusing the user.

Other problems were encountered in binary alloys where some of these are intermetallic compounds and the atoms occur in stoichiometric ratios; in doping agents, where an impurity is introduced in a definite and controlled amount; and in materials not usually thought of as semiconductors or insulators, but which become so under certain conditions (e.g., the alkali halides which exhibit some insulating properties, but which, under ultraviolet irradiation, become semiconductors).

Similar problems were encountered with the properties. It became necessary to issue glossaries of selected properties and effects to achieve agreement among technical personnel. After compiling lists of properties, decisions had to be made as to which were synonyms and near synonyms, and which would be subsumed under others. In semiconductors, for example, a list of 140 electronic properties was reduced to 29, with the rest subsumed under these.

In its entirety to date, over 12,000 names of materials have been considered for use in the prime indexing vocabulary. Of these, approximately 3500 have now been entered into the indexing vocabulary. In addition, approximately 4000 of eventual use to the Center have been determined, and it is anticipated that most of the rest will eventually find their way into the syndetic apparatus as "see-references".

The Index

After an item is finally appraised for inclusion in the system, it is assigned an "accession number" by which it will be identified through the routines of work flow and in the final indexing system. It is then abstracted and indexed by subject specialists with both functions being performed at the same time by the same person. Guides are furnished to assure a continuity of presentation from item to item. The abstracts are not conventional abstracts, but rather refer to the experimental data.

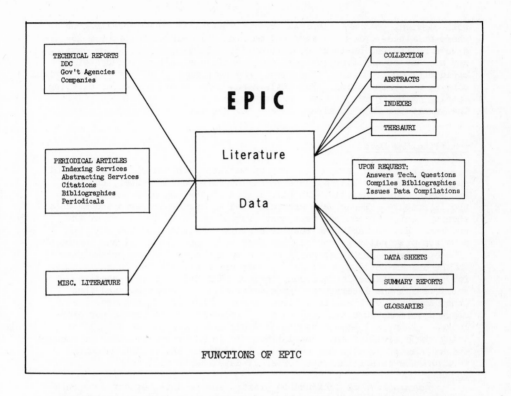

FUNCTIONS OF EPIC

The indexing system itself can be called a manual modified coordinate index. It is composed of a file and a master printout from an IBM 1401 computer. The file is a file of abstract cards, each card containing a complete bibliographic entry and the abstract. The print-out is the Descriptor File, consisting of alphabetically arranged descriptors. This file is divided first into the major categories of materials. It then consists of "pre-coordinated" descriptors of one material or one material and one property (e.g., INDIUM ARSENIDE - ABSORPTION). Under each of these descriptors are listed the accession numbers of articles appropriate to that descriptor.

Retrieval involving more than one property or material at a time is accomplished by matching the accession numbers under the relevant descriptors. If the same number is found under two or more descriptors, that article deals with both or a combination of both descriptors.

Although retrieval is a manual process, the accession numbers are posted using an IBM 1401 computer. This provides the capability of producing tab runs of materials and properties and significantly reduces both clerical cost and clerical error. The latter is especially true where multiple copies are made and maintained. Since the program is always maintained up-to-date, it provides a back-up file. A new catalog may be made at any time, either for an additional set or because of accidental destruction of the first, and at a much lower cost than clerical copying or reproduction. Yet while a new catalog or part of an existing catalog is being run, it is unnecessary to remove a card from a file. The Descriptor File is always intact for users.

Compiling the Data

The second part of the dichotomic approach and the real value of such a highly-specialized, data-gathering information center, has been the evaluation, analysis, and compilation of the experimental data from the literature. These data are published as summary reports and as data sheets. This, of course, is a most crucial and difficult part of the program. How valuable the results might be depends upon how well the data are originally presented, and even more upon the skill and judgement of the subject specialist assigned the work. Articles are accumulated in the system until a sufficient number are available on one material for adequate evaluation and compilation. The index is then used to retrieve all the literature on the material to be compiled, and then other sources, such as the bibliographies within the literature, are checked to make sure that valuable and relevant literature is not over-looked. Then, all of the assembled items are given to the specialist doing the evaluation and compilation. It is his responsibility to compare the associated data in the assembled literature, and to determine the form and the extent that the series of data sheets will take.

Evaluation is confined to primary source data, except when only secondary citations are available. Frequently, it is found that equally valid data are available from several sources, and all are given. When judged questionable, however, data are rejected - most frequently because of faulty or dubious measurements, unknown sample composition, or occa-sionally because more reliable data are available from another source. The selection of data is based upon that which is judged to be most repre-sentative, precise, and reliable, and which covers the widest range of variables.

After the data are thoroughly analyzed and evaluated, they are compiled into a series of data sheets, which present them in their optimum form. Primarily, this will be curves or tabular form. Where possible, graphs are adapted directly from the original sources; but if this is not possible, they may be drawn from data compiled from the articles. Frequently, it has been found that data can be shown best when synthesized from many articles. In general, the most technically promising materials have been chosen first for compilation, with an average of about 30 data sheets in final form for each of the materials.

6

AIR FORCE MATERIALS LABORATORY
RESEARCH AND TECHNOLOGY DIVISION
AIR FORCE SYSTEMS COMMAND

E LECTRONIC
P ROPERTIES
I NFORMATION
C ENTER

PREPARED BY ELECTRONIC PROPERTIES INFORMATION CENTER • HUGHES AIRCRAFT COMPANY, CULVER CITY, CALIFORNIA

ZINC SULFIDE   DECEMBER 1963

Mobility

Symbol	Value (cm^2/V sec)	Type	Ref.
μ	∿10-100		3307
μ	∿100	hexagonal or cubic	2586
μ_n	∿120 (110-140)	hexagonal, some chlorine-doped $\sigma \sim 10^{-10}$ (ohm cm)$^{-1}$ T=300°K	2972
μ	∿100	hexagonal, single crystal wurtzite	2525

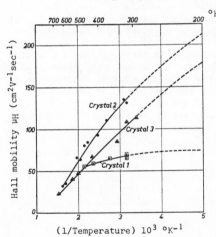

Electron Hall mobility as a function of temperature for single crystal, hexagonal, chlorine-doped zinc sulfide samples.

[Ref. 2972]

TYPICAL DATA SHEET

7

To date, series of data sheets have been compiled on the following materials: Cadmium Telluride, Indium Phosphide, Indium Telluride, Magnesium Silicide, Polyethylene Terephthalate, Polytetrafluoroethylene, Polytrifluorochloroethylene, Zinc Telluride, Indium Arsenide, Aluminum Antimonide, Gallium Phosphide, Gallium Antimonide, Lead Telluride, Magnesium Stannide, Gallium Arsenide, Lead Selenide, Silicon, Indium Antimonide, Steatite, Beryllium Oxide, Cadmium Sulfide, Magnesium Oxide, Silicone Rubber, Cordierite, Forsterite, Pyroceram, Germanium, Zinc Selenide, Zinc Oxide, Cadmium Selenide, Zinc Sulfide, Aluminum Oxide, Borosilicate Glasses, Aluminosilicate Glasses, and Fluorocarbon Gases.

The value of an information center in taking a data-oriented approach can be readily seen through the following statistics. For every 1000 titles which have been discovered through examination of indexing or abstracting services, government report compilations, examinations of bibliographies, or similar means, approximately 300 are selected for closer examination. These 300 are examined in their entirety by either acquiring them or by examining them in periodicals or other compilations available in libraries of the area. Of these 300, approximately 100 are acquired, and approximately 25 of these result in data sufficiently valuable to be included in data sheets.

Use of the Center

Use of the Center is not restricted to government agencies or their contractors. EPIC is available to all who wish data on the electrical and electronic properties of materials. To date, our capabilities are primarily in the semiconductor and insulator fields, but we are rapidly acquiring literature in the other categories, and we anticipate a considerable output of data sheets in all categories during this coming year. Over 1963, we not only helped many members of DOD agencies in their materials applications programs, but we assisted many research workers in both government and private industry as well. It's interesting to note that EPIC has answered one question from a high school student, and has assisted one PhD candidate in obtaining his degree.

8

THE FUTURE

At the present time, additional studies are being accomplished. The bibliographic entry and abstract are being prepared on punched paper tape through means of a Flexowriter, and it is anticipated that this information will soon be stored on magnetic tape for computer use. This will not only allow automatic literature searching, but also printouts of the bibliographic information by title and author as well as accession number, with or without the abstract.

New ways are being explored for storing more of the data as well as the literature for computer use. Access facets, which will include several levels of information, beginning with the article containing the data and running through groups of data associated with one material or one material and property down to the individual point established by the original experiment, are being carefully evaluated. Complete cross-referencing between facets will provide optimum use of the data.

Although the program is slanted toward materials applications, the data processing techniques which have been evolved are making it valuable for other uses, such as: (1) master tab runs of materials and properties can be produced, (2) valuable statistical counts can be made, such as average number of descriptors per article or average number of articles in the system per material and property, (3) state-of-the-art surveys can be easily accomplished, for the system will indicate not only areas where research has been done, but also areas where gaps in the literature, and therefore to some extent in research, occur, and (4) a measure of the growth of research activities in the field can be developed.

9

BIBLIOGRAPHY

Johnson, H. Thayne. "A Dichotomic Approach to the Retrieval of Specialized
    Information." Southern California Special Libraries Association
    Bulletin, Vol. 25, No. 3, Spring, 1964.

Johnson, H. Thayne, Emil Schafer, and Everett M. Wallace. Electrical and
    Electronic Properties of Materials, Information Retrieval Program,
    Technical Documentary Report No. ASD-TDR-62-539, Directorate of Mate-
    rials and Processes, Aeronautical Systems Division, Wright-Patterson
    Air Force Base, Ohio, June 1962.

Johnson, H. Thayne. How the Electronic Properties Information Center
    Meets User Requirements in a Highly Specialized Field. Presented
    at the Annual Business Meeting of the Southern California Chapter
    of the American Documentation Institute, April 13, 1964.

Johnson, H. Thayne. "An Information Retrieval Program on the Electrical
    and Electronic Properties of Materials," presented at the Materials
    Information Symposium, Dayton, Ohio, November 28-29, 1962.

Johnson, H. Thayne. "Next, the Automatic Library", Vectors, Vol. IV,
    No. 2 (Second Quarter, 1962), Hughes Aircraft Company.

Johnson, H. Thayne, and Miles C. Pine. A Punched Card Program for Posting
    Descriptor Cards in Information Retrieval Systems, Report No. SRS 576,
    Hughes Aircraft Company, Culver City, Calif., September 1962.

Johnson, H. Thayne, and Lou E. Vaughn. A Theoretical Information Re-
    trieval System for Retrieving Highly Specific Materials Data, Report No.
    SRS 577, Hughes Aircraft Company, Culver City, Calif., September 1962.

Schafer, Emil. Insulation Materials Descriptors Used in the Electrical
    and Electronic Properties of Materials Information Retrieval Program,
    Special Report No. 1 (Contract AF33(616)-8438), Hughes Aircraft Co.,
    Culver City, Calif., July 1962.

Schafer, Emil. Semiconductor Materials Descriptors Used in the Electrical
    and Electronic Properties of Materials Information Retrieval Program,
    Special Report No. 2 (Contract AF33(616)-8438), Hughes Aircraft Co.,
    Culver City, Calif., September 1962.

Wallace, Everett M. Information Retrieval Program, Electronic/Electrical
    Properties of Materials, First, Second, and Third Quarterly Reports
    (Contract AF33(616)-8438), Hughes Aircraft Co., Culver City, Calif.,
    October 1961, January 1962, April 1962.

Index